The Way of the World

The Way of the World

Bernard J. Weiss
Senior Author
Reading and Linguistics

Eldonna L. Evertts
Language Arts

Loreli Olson Steuer
Reading and Linguistics

Susan B. Cruikshank
Reading and Language Arts

Lyman C. Hunt
General Editor—Satellite Books

Holt
Basic
Reading

Level 10

HOLT, RINEHART AND WINSTON, PUBLISHERS
New York • Toronto • Mexico City • London • Sydney • Tokyo

ISBN 0-03-061392-2
345   071   9876543

Acknowledgments:

Grateful acknowledgment is given to the following authors and publishers:

Addison-Wesley Publishing Company, Inc., for "The Flying Patchwork Quilt," adapted from *The Flying Patchwork Quilt,* a Young Scott Book by Barbara Brenner. Copyright © 1965 by Barbara Brenner. Used by permission.

Atheneum Publishers, Inc., for "Until I Saw the Sea," from *I Feel the Same Way* by Lilian Moore. Copyright © 1967 by Lilian Moore. Used by permission.

The William Collins + World Publishing Co. Inc., and The Bodley Head Ltd., for "Fumio and the Dolphins," adapted from their translation of *Fumio and the Dolphins* by Chinoko Nakatani. Copyright © 1970 by The Bodley Head, Ltd. Used by permission.

Thomas Y. Crowell Company, for adaptation of the text of *Amy's Goose* by Efner Tudor Holmes. Copyright © 1977 by Efner Tudor Holmes. For "Company Clothes," from *In One Door and Out the Other* by Aileen Fisher. Copyright © 1969 by Aileen Fisher. Used by permission.

Coward, McCann & Geoghegan, Inc., for "A Home in the Desert," adapted from *Oasis of the Stars* by Olga Economakis. Copyright © 1965 by Olga Economakis. Used by permission.

Follett Publishing Company, for "The Collector," from *That Was Summer* by Marci Ridlon. Copyright © 1969 by Marci Ridlon. Used by permission.

Grosset & Dunlap, Inc., for "I Can Fly," from *At the Top of My Voice and Other Poems* by Felice Holman. Copyright © 1970 by Felice Holman. Used by permission.

Harvey House, Inc., for "The Sunflower Garden," adapted from *The Sunflower Garden* by Janice May Udry. Copyright © 1969 by Harvey House, Inc. Used by permission.

Macmillan Publishing Co. Inc., for "February Twilight," from *Collected Poems of Sara Teasdale.* Copyright 1926 by Macmillan Publishing Co., Inc., renewed 1954 by Mamie T. Wheless. For "The Beaver," from *Toucans Two and Other Poems* by Jack Prelutsky. Copyright © 1967 by Jack Prelutsky. Used by permission.

McGraw-Hill Book Company, for "Valentine for Earth," from *The Little Whistler* by Frances Frost. Copyright 1949 by McGraw-Hill, Inc. Used by permission.

Thomas Nelson & Sons, for "In the Country," from *That's Why* by Aileen Fisher. Copyright 1946, renewed © 1974 by Aileen Fisher. Used by permission of the author.

Parents' Magazine Press, for an adaptation of *Hurray For Captain Jane!* by Sam Reavin. Text copyright © 1971 by Sam Reavin. For "Such Is the Way of the World," adapted from *Such is the Way of the World* by Benjamin Elkin. Copyright © 1968 by Benjamin Elkin. For "Martin for Mayor," adapted from *Butch Elects a Mayor* by Helene Hanff. Copyright © 1969 by Helene Hanff. For "Granny's Fish Story," adapted from *Granny's Fish Story* by Phyllis LaFarge. Text copyright © 1975 by Phillis LaFarge. Used by permission.

Prentice-Hall, Inc., and McIntosh and Otis, Inc., for "Ramu and the Kite," adapted from *Ramu and the Kite* by Mehlli Gobhai. Copyright © 1968 by Prentice-Hall, Inc. Used by permission.

Rand McNally & Company, for "Undersea," by Marchette Chute, from *Child Life Magazine.* Copyright 1935, renewed © 1963 by Rand McNally Company. Used by permission.

Russell & Volkening, Inc., as agents for the author, for "Way Down Deep," from *Hello and Good-Bye* by Mary Ann Hoberman. Copyright © 1959 by Mary Ann Hoberman. Used by permission.

Scholastic Magazines, Inc., for *Charlie The Tramp,* by Russell Hoban. Copyright © 1966 by Russell Hoban. Used by permission.

Albert Whitman & Co., for an adaptation of "Mary Jo's Grandmother," from *Mary Jo's Grandmother* by Janice May Udry. Text copyright © 1970 by Janice May Udry. For "Statues," from *Town and Countryside Poems* by John Travers Moore. Copyright © 1968. Used by permission.

Art Credits:

Victor Valla, pages 14—21
Miriam Schottland, pages 22—23
Museum of the City of New York, page 34
Diane de Groat, pages 96—101, 146—147, 169, 286—287
Sven Lindman, pages 44, 146, 234
    (career graphics)
Carol Lieterman, pages 44—45
Marie DeJohn, pages 46—58
Bernie D'Andrea, pages 60—75
Bernice Myers, pages 76—91
Tad Krumeich, pages 93, 125, 203
Holden Weintraub, page 103
Bob Goldstein, pages 104—108
Symeon Shimin, pages 110—123

Tim and Greg Hildebrandt, pages 124, 172—189
Robert Jackson, pages 126—138
Marie Michal, page 139
Charles Lily, pages 140—145
Denver Gillen, pages 148—160
Jeannette Kehl, pages 190—191
Muriel Wood, pages 192—202
Ethel Gold, pages 204—217
Carolyn Bracken, page 219
Ivan Powell, pages 220—227
Susan Swan, pages 234—235
Kyuzo Tsugami, pages 236—245
Jane Clark, pages 246—255
Jerry Pinkney, pages 258—285

Cover design by James Endicott
Unit Opener designs by Karen Akoff

Photo Credits:

p. 34 Museum of the City of New York. p. 35 Diane de Groat. p. 36—37 Museum of the City of New York. p. 38 top, Museum of the City of New York; bottom, Rene Burri/Magnum. p. 39 top, bottom left, Diane de Groat; bottom right, Ernest Haas. p. 40 Freda Leinwand. p. 41 left, Charles Harbutt; right, Freda Leinwand. p. 42—43 Ingbet. p. 44 top, HRW Photo by Ken Lax; bottom, Pro Pix/Monkmeyer Press Photo. p. 45 top, Charles Harbutt/Magnum; bottom, Hal McKusiek/dpi. p. 59 Ingbet. p. 92 NASA. p. 102, 109 George Senty. p. 146 top, Yoram Kahana from Peter Arnold; bottom, Courtesy General Electric. p. 147 Dr. E.R. Degginger. p. 218 Leslie Bauman. p. 228—233 the family of Elizabeth Levy. p. 234 top, Shostal Associates; bottom, Maxwell Coplan. p. 235 top left, Dr. E.R. Degginger; top right, HRW Photo by Russell Dian; bottom, Courtesy of American Airlines. p. 256 Ingbet.

Table of Contents

1

THE EARTH
WE LIVE ON

The world is so full
   of a number of things,
I'm sure we should all
   be as happy as kings.

—Robert Louis Stevenson

Such Is the Way of the World

Benjamin Elkin

This was a big day for Desta. For the
first time he was in charge of his father's cows.
He was in charge all by himself. Desta walked
along with the cows. His pet monkey, Jima,
sat on his arm. All was right with Desta's world.

But the world does not stand still. Things
are not always the same. Out of nowhere came
a big dog. It jumped at Jima. The monkey
climbed a tree and was gone. Desta couldn't
see the monkey anywhere.

Desta was so upset he began to cry.
He cried so much that the cows began to run.
Soon they were gone, too. But Desta forgot about
the cows. He wanted to find his pet monkey,
Jima.

"Don't cry," said the owner of the dog. "Such
is the way of the world that dogs must hunt
and monkeys must run away. Here, you may have
this game to pay for your monkey," he said.
And he put the game under Desta's arm.

Down the road Desta saw some men sitting
around a fire. Maybe they knew where Jima was!
As Desta ran to the men, he tripped over one
of them who was sleeping near the fire. The game
fell out of his hands. It fell into the fire.

The man got to his feet and said, "I should
not have been sleeping so near the fire. I'm
sorry about your game. But it did make our
fire much brighter. Such is the way
of the world. Here, you may have this pot
to pay for the game." And he put the pot
on Desta's head.

X A quick look showed Desta that Jima wasn't there. "Maybe something horrible has happened to Jima," thought Desta. "I must not stand here. I must find him right away."

X Desta ran until he came to a small town. Maybe Jima was there! Desta saw the men in the town getting ready for a hunt. All the men were wearing fur and feathers. But Desta did not see anyone with a pet monkey.

X A man reached for the pot on Desta's head. "I don't have my drum," he said. "Stand here and let me drum on your pot."

But the man hit the pot only a few times before it broke. "Such is the way of the world. I have tried an army of pots, and not one has ever made a good drum. I'm sorry I broke your pot. Here, take this knife to pay for it."

Desta took the knife and went on looking for Jima.

Along the way Desta stopped to watch a man dig a hole with his hands. "I'm looking for my pet monkey," he told the man. "Did you see any monkeys today?"

"My boy," said the man, "when you watch goats, you see only goats. Could I have your knife for a minute to help me dig this hole?"

Desta gave the knife to the man, and he started to dig. But the knife hit a stone and broke.

"I'm very sorry," said the man. "But such
is the way of the world. Here, take this spear
to pay for the knife."

X Desta took the spear. Now here was
something that might help him save Jima.
He saw some hunters ahead of him,
and he ran to ask them about his monkey.

A hunter at once reached out for Desta's spear.
"You must give us this spear. We saw a tiger
near our town, and we need all the spears
we can get. But first I want to try it out."

The spear was very old, and it broke when it hit
a tree.

X "Such is the way of the world," said the hunter.
"It is far better to find out now that the spear
doesn't work than when we come face to face
with the tiger."

The man turned to Desta and said, "I'm sorry
I broke your spear. In this bag is a little monkey
that I found. Take the monkey for the spear.
The monkey will be a good pet for you."

"A monkey," thought Desta. "Could it be Jima?"

Desta opened the bag. There was Jima. Desta picked up his pet. He thought of nothing but the joy of having Jima back.

Desta started for home. But then he remembered his father's cows. There they were ahead of him, going home without him. Desta ran to catch up with the cows.

X Near the house Father and Mother looked up and saw Desta bringing home the cows. And walking beside Desta was his pet monkey, Jima. Desta looked very happy. All was right with his world.

Father turned to Mother and said, "We were right to give Desta that little monkey. There is nothing like a good pet to help a boy do his work well. Such is the way of the world."

The Sunflower Garden

Janice May Udry

PART ONE

The Seeds

Pipsa was a little girl who lived with her family in a small village. Pipsa had five brothers. Four of them were older than Pipsa. But one was still small.

Pipsa's father was proud of his sons. He was proud of how well the four older ones could swim. He didn't notice how well Pipsa took care of her small brother. Her father was proud of how well his four older sons fished. He didn't notice all the berries Pipsa picked.

Pipsa's father was proud that his four older sons could hunt. They came home with lots of birds and rabbits. He didn't notice the straw bags that Pipsa made. He didn't notice how Pipsa helped her mother make clothes.

Pipsa's father showed his sons how to do things. He was proud of his sons. And he told them so. But he never told Pipsa how proud he was of her.

Pipsa's mother was proud of her. At times she said, "You did well, my Pipsa."

In the spring Pipsa helped her mother plant corn and beans. How her brothers loved to eat! But they did not help with the planting.

This year Pipsa could not wait for spring to come. She had some seeds in a small box. They were sunflower seeds. Pipsa had picked the seeds last fall, when the family had gone to another village. That was the first time Pipsa had ever seen sunflowers. She did not know flowers grew so big! She could not wait to plant her seeds.

24

One of the girls in the other village had
shown Pipsa how to make cakes from the seeds.
And she had told Pipsa about the wonderful oil
they made. The girls in the village put the
sunflower oil on their hair.

Now spring was here. Pipsa was going to grow
sunflowers. But she would have to do all the
work herself. Her mother would not have time
to help her. Pipsa started to dig in the dirt.
She would plant the seeds at the right time.

One night Pipsa heard her father say it
would soon rain. Pipsa went to the place she
had picked for her garden. She planted the
seeds. The rain would water them.

Each day Pipsa looked at the dirt. She thought
about the seeds. "Are the seeds any good?
Did I plant them right? Will they grow?" she
asked herself.

Day after day Pipsa went to her garden.
She watched for a sign of green. And then one
day she saw it. Soon the garden was filled
with small plants.

It was a good summer for plants. By
the middle of the summer, most of the sunflowers
were filled with seeds. Soon it would be time
to pick them. Then Pipsa and her mother would
make the cakes. They would make hair. oil, too.

People in Pipsa's village came to look
at Pipsa's garden. They liked the big, bright
flowers. Most of the plants grew two times
as big as Pipsa.

The birds loved Pipsa's sunflowers, too.
Keeping them away from the seeds was work.

27

PART TWO

The Snake

One night Pipsa was working in her garden.
Her little brother was with her. All at once
Pipsa saw a snake. She quickly put down her hoe.
Then she looked for her brother. He didn't see
the snake.

Pipsa had to keep the snake away from
her brother. She picked up the hoe. Then
she walked quietly to the snake. Pipsa
had never seen a snake that big. But she knew
she must kill it before it killed her brother.
Pipsa had never been so afraid. What if she
missed? What if she only made the snake mad?

28

Pipsa hit the snake's head with the hoe. She didn't stop to see if she had killed it. She hit the snake again and again.

Pipsa's little brother was afraid. He jumped to his feet.

"Run, Little Brother, run!" cried Pipsa.

The boy ran crying to his mother. Soon Pipsa's mother, father, and brothers came. When they saw what had happened, they were surprised. Who would think that Pipsa could kill such a big snake. Pipsa saw that they were proud of her.

And for the first time Pipsa's father said to her, "You did well, Pipsa. You are a brave child."

Pipsa's father looked around at the sunflower garden. He had never seen it before.

"What are you growing?" he asked.

"Sunflowers, Father," Pipsa told him.

"What are they for?" her father asked.

Pipsa told him that soon they would have good
little cakes from the seeds if she could keep
the birds away. And she told him how they could
make hair oil from the seeds, too.

Pipsa's father looked again at the big sunflowers.
Then he looked at Pipsa as if he had never seen
her before. He put his big hand on her head.

"I'm very proud of you," he said.

The next day Pipsa's father told her brothers
to take turns helping Pipsa. They could keep
the birds away from the sunflower seeds.

At last the seeds were ready. All the people
In the village came to watch Pipsa pound the seeds
into little cakes. When they were ready, Pipsa
gave everyone some cake to eat. They all thought
the cakes were very good.

Pipsa showed the girls how to make oil
from the seeds. They put it on their hair.
She gave the people some seeds. The next spring
they all grew sunflowers.

The people in the village were proud of
Pipsa. She had given them a new plant and
new ideas. They called her the "Sunflower Girl."

The years went by. The Indians in Pipsa's village grew more and more sunflowers. Pipsa grew up. She had a little girl of her own. The Indians told Pipsa's girl of how Pipsa had started the first sunflower garden in their village

Frederick L. Olmsted

Elizabeth Levy

Do you have a park where you live? If you do, did you ever think, "How did a park get here?" Your park did not just happen. It had to be planned. Someone had to make it happen.

Frederick L. Olmsted was a man who planned parks. He lived a long time ago. He lived before cities were as big as they are now. But he knew that cities would grow. He knew that the people who lived in cities would need parks. They would need places to play games. They would need places to walk. Frederick planned beautiful parks. He planned parks with trees and flowers.

But there was a time when Frederick did not even think of parks. For a long time, his friends thought that he would never do anything.

"When is Frederick going to find something to do?" they would ask.

Frederick went away to school, but he did not stay there. He worked in a store for a time. He didn't like that at all! So he took a trip to Europe. He stayed in Europe for a year.

When Frederick came home from Europe, he went to work on a farm. He liked being a farmer. His friends thought, "At last Frederick has found something that he likes to do." His father was happy, too. So his father got Frederick his own farm.

Frederick was not a farmer for long. Soon he took another trip to Europe. This time he wrote a book about his trip. Most of all, he wrote about the wonderful parks he saw in the cities.

When Frederick came back to this country, he tried to farm again. But again, he didn't farm for long.

Frederick tried all kinds of work. He could not find a thing that he really liked to do.

So Frederick went back home to New York City. When he got there, his friends told him about plans for a park in the city. When he heard about the park, Frederick said, "I'd like to have something to do with that."

There was a contest to see who could plan the best park. Frederick wanted to be in the contest. He worked with a friend on a plan for the park. They thought about what the people would like to have in a city park.

Should a walk in the park be like a walk on a street? Or like a walk in the woods? Should a park have places to play games? Or places for monuments? Should a park have hills? Should it be one big park or lots of small parks?

From his trips to Europe, Frederick knew a lot about parks. He hoped the park would be as lovely as the parks in Europe. From his farm days, he knew a lot about the country. He hoped the park would look like the country. So Frederick and his friend planned to bring the country to New York City.

Frederick and his friend won the contest.

Frederick's park is in New York City.
It's called Central Park. There are places
to play all kinds of games. There are
places for monuments. There are hills and
trees and even woods. When you walk there,
it's like a walk in the country.

You don't have to look out for cars
in Central Park. You can play all kinds
of games. You can even look at bears.
They are in cages so they can't bite you.
You can look at flowers and trees. There
are all kinds of plants in the park. And
birds come there from all over. There is
something in Central Park for everyone.

People from all over the country came to see
Central Park. They liked the park. So they
asked Frederick to plan parks for their cities.
And he did. Today there are parks planned by
Frederick Olmsted in all parts of our country.

Frederick Olmsted liked his work.
He planned parks for the rest of his life.
And no one ever asked again, "When is
Frederick going to find something to do?"

Statues

I wonder what happens after dark
   to statues in the park.
Do they dance and sing
   in the joy of spring?
Do they run and play
   till the light of day?
I wonder what happens to statues
   in the park.

—*John Travers Moore*

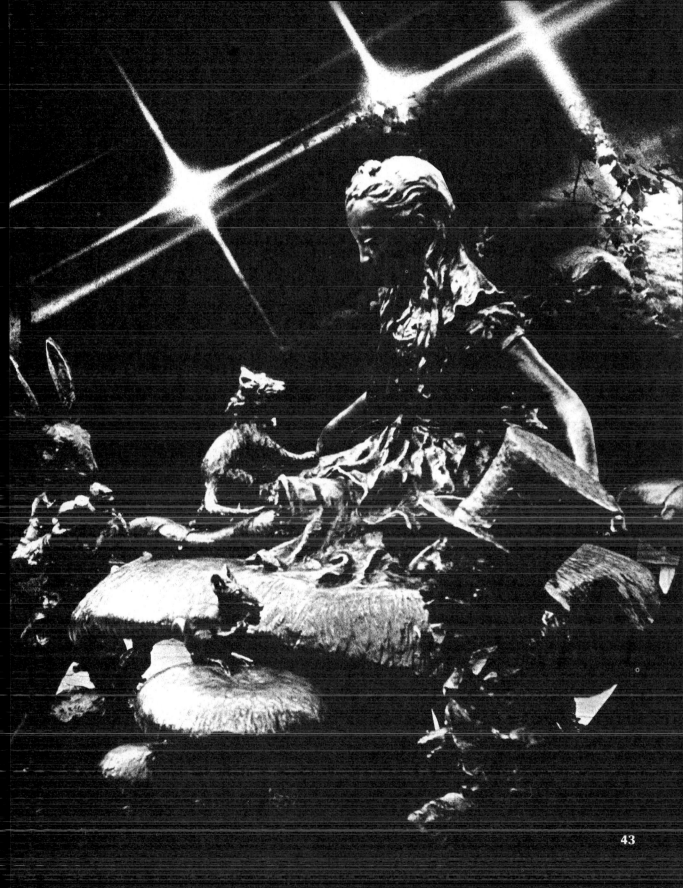

The Earth We Live On

The earth is our home. It's the place where we live. It's the place where we work and play.

These people are the "builders" of the earth.

These builders are called *architects.* Here they are working on plans for a new building. They want the building to be strong and useful. They also want it to be beautiful.

These builders are called *carpenters.* They are using special tools to put up a group of wooden houses. The houses will be winter homes for Eskimo families in Alaska.

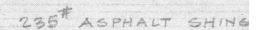

235# ASPHALT SHING

ALUM GUTTER

These special builders are building a skyscraper. They are using steel to make the "skeleton" of the building. Each piece of steel has a number that tells the builder where to put it. As the steel skeleton rises, other workers finish the lower floors.

Landscape architects design outdoor spaces. They plan trees and grassy areas. They plan walks and ponds. They plan parks and zoos. This landscape architect wants to see that her plans come true!

Would you like to be a builder of the earth? What would you like to build?

Mary Jo's Grandmother

Janice May Udry

PART ONE
Grandmother's Fall

Mary Jo's grandmother lived in a little house in the country. She lived alone, even though she was old.

Mary Jo's mother and father did not want her grandmother to live alone. They had tried and tried to get her to move into town.

"You should not be living all alone way out here," Mary Jo's mother would say. "You don't have a telephone. Why, you don't even have a neighbor nearby."

But Grandmother did not want to move. "I've lived in this house most of my life," she would say. "I'm too old to move now. I'm happy here."

X Every Christmas, all of the family went to Grandmother's house for the day. But this Christmas was a very special one for Mary Jo. For the first time she would be staying with Grandmother for a few days.

X Christmas came. As always, it was a family day. First, the family ate. Then, there were games and singing. It was a long day.

X After the family had left, Mary Jo and Grandmother were ready for bed. Just before she fell asleep, Mary Jo saw great flakes of snow falling like feathers outside the window.

The morning after Christmas Day, Mary Jo went into the kitchen. Great flakes of snow were still falling.

"This is the most snow I've ever seen here at Christmas time," said Grandmother. She was putting biscuits into the oven. "Mary Jo," she said, "take some seeds out to the birds. I have to go to the pantry."

When Mary Jo came back, Grandmother was still in the pantry. From the open pantry door, she heard a cry.

"Mary Jo!" Grandmother called.

"Grandmother, what happened?" said Mary Jo, running to the door. She looked down into the room. Her grandmother was on the pantry floor.

"I tripped on the step," Grandmother moaned. "I can't get up!"

"I'm coming! I'll help you!" said Mary Jo.

"Take the biscuits out of the oven first," said Grandmother.

Mary Jo ran to the oven and took the biscuits out. Then she ran back to the pantry. She tried to help her grandmother up. But Grandmother moaned.

"No, Mary Jo, don't try to move me. It's my left leg. I can't move it."

Mary Jo looked around at the dark little pantry. It was cold. She ran back through the kitchen and into a bedroom. There, she got some blankets and a pillow. She put the blankets around her grandmother and the pillow under her head.

"Good girl," said Grandmother. "I feel better with the blankets and pillow. I'm so happy you are here, Mary Jo. Just let me rest now. I'll be all right. You go and have some biscuits before they get cold."

Grandmother put her head back on the pillow and closed her eyes.

XMary Jo went back into the kitchen and ate some biscuits. She looked out the window at the great flakes of falling snow. "I don't even have my boots here," Mary Jo thought. She went back into the pantry. Grandmother opened her eyes and moaned.

XShe knew that she must go for help because her grandmother did not have a telephone. There was no neighbor nearby. She would have to walk to the main road. On a day like this, no one would be on the little side road where Grandmother lived.

X"I'm going to the main road for help," said Mary Jo.

"In all this snow?" said Grandmother.

"I can do it," said Mary Jo.

Grandmother put her head back on the pillow again. "I guess I'll have to let you go, Mary Jo," she said. "But put some warm clothes on."

"Yes, Grandmother," said Mary Jo. "You rest. I won't be long."

"I'll be all right," said Grandmother.

Mary Jo found some old boots. She made them fit by putting newspaper in them. She put on warm clothes. At last she was ready to go. She looked in on Grandmother. But Grandmother was asleep. Mary Jo made sure that the back door was closed and walked out into the snow.

PART TWO
A Long Walk

The snow had stopped falling. The sky was clear. But Mary Jo could feel the wind on her face. She walked as fast as she could. But it took a long time to reach even the side road. When she got there, she saw that no car had been along.

"Oh, if only Grandmother had a neighbor nearby," she thought.

Mary Jo walked along the side road. By now the snow had started to get into her big boots. Sometimes she felt she could not take another step. She had never felt so much alone as she did in that cold, white world. She hadn't even seen a squirrel.

At last Mary Jo reached the main road. She could see that no cars had been along. Her legs had never felt so tired before. She would have to rest before she started out again.

Mary Jo sat down in the snow, keeping her eyes on the road. After a few minutes had gone by, she saw something. It was dark, and it was moving. Mary Jo looked for a minute. Then she jumped up and waved.

"It's the snowplow!" she cried. Though no one was there, she wanted to hear her own voice. "It's the snowplow!" she cried, and waved again.

"I don't think they can see me," she thought. She waved again. Then someone waved back.

Mary Jo felt cold. She jumped up and down to keep warm, even though her legs were tired.

At last the snowplow was there. The driver opened the door. "What are you doing out here, little girl?" he asked.

Mary Jo told him what had happened. "Can you call my father in town?" she asked.

"We'll be happy to do that," said the man. "But what about you? You can't walk all the way back in this snow."

"I must get back to my grandmother," said
Mary Jo.

"Did you ever ride on a snowplow?" the man asked.

Mary Jo shook her head.

"Here, climb up," the driver said. "We'll
clear the side road and get you back to your
grandmother's house. Then we'll go on to the
next house and call your father."

"It's a good thing you were on the corner,"
the driver went on. "We weren't going to clear
this side road today. We only clear out the main
road the first day after a big snow like this."

Mary Jo got down from the snowplow and went into the house. She told her grandmother what had happened.

Soon after, Mary Jo looked out the window. She could see two cars. Her mother, father, and brother got out of one. A doctor with a dark bag got out of the other.

"They're here, Grandmother!" Mary Jo called, and she ran to open the door.

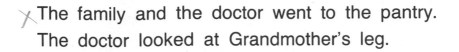The family and the doctor went to the pantry.
The doctor looked at Grandmother's leg.

"We'll have you on your feet in no time,"
she said.

"It's so good to see you," Grandmother said.
"I don't know what would have happened if
Mary Jo had not been here. She was so brave
to go out in that storm!"

"We are very proud of Mary Jo," said Father.
He put his arm around her.

Mary Jo was very happy. She would not forget
this day.

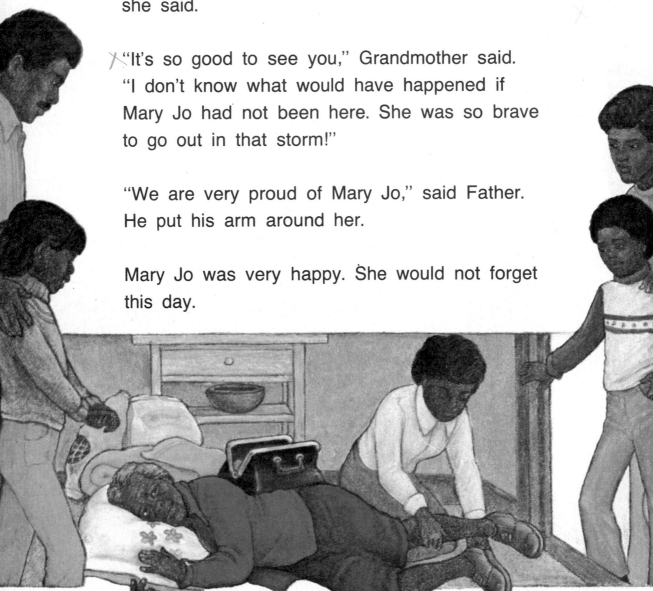

Company Clothes

I had to dress up
and not wear jeans
or even my comfortable
in-betweens,
and not wear boots
or my zebra sweater
because Mother said
she'd had a letter
and someone she knew
when she was small
was stopping to call
so I had to look better.

And what do you know!
Their boy was John…
And he had jeans
and a sweater on!
So I changed mine back
in one-two-three,
to keep my company
company.

—Aileen Fisher

59

Martin for Mayor

Helene Hanff

PART ONE
Butch Wants to Help

Butch Martin sat down to eat. Butch's father said, "I have news for you. They want me to run for mayor."

"That's great!" said Butch's mother.

"It will mean a lot of work," said Mr. Martin.

"I'll help you," said Butch.

"Butch," said his father. "You mean well. But every time you help something happens."

"What do you mean?" asked Butch.

"Once you helped me," said Butch's mother. "You helped me with my groceries. You took the groceries home. But you didn't take the right ones. You took some other woman's groceries. She didn't say thank you when she got them back."

"I think you should wait until you're a little older to work in an election campaign," said Butch's father.

"If Dad doesn't want my help, then he can just get elected mayor by himself," thought Butch.

One day Mr. Martin took Butch downtown.
Butch saw a big sign in a store window.
On the sign was, "Martin for Mayor."

"Come in," said Mr. Martin.
"This is where we work for my election.
This is campaign headquarters."

Butch went into the headquarters. He
saw signs all around. Campaign buttons
and newspapers were on the tables.

"Who are all these people?" asked Butch.
"Why are they here?"

"We're here to help your father get elected
mayor," said a woman.

"May I help?" asked Butch.

"This is Mrs. Stein," said Mr. Martin.
"Now, Butch, please. No help. Every time
you help, something happens."

"What can happen?" asked Mrs. Stein.
"Let him help me."

"All right," said Mr. Martin. "But with Butch
things happen." He turned to talk to some people.
Then he went off to a meeting with them.

Butch folded letters with Mrs. Stein. "Vote, Martin for Mayor" was on the letters.

Soon it was time for lunch. Mrs. Stein said, "Time to eat. I'll get us something next door."

"I'll go for you, Mrs. Stein," said Butch.

"No, thank you," said Mrs. Stein. "I need the air. I haven't been out all morning."

"It's hot in here," Butch thought after Mrs. Stein had gone. "There's a fan. I'll air out the room the way Mother does." Butch opened the back door. He turned on the fan. It was standing in one corner of the room. The fan did air out the room. But it did more than that. It made the letters, papers, and signs fly through the air, too. Out the door they flew.

The papers flew into the garden next door. People were eating there. One man put a spoon into a bowl. He fished out a letter. "Vote, Martin for Mayor," he read. One letter flew right on top of the cake a little girl was eating. Some letters hit a waiter in the face. The waiter tripped. Five lunches fell on the floor.

Butch saw Mrs. Stein come into headquarters. She was in a hurry. In one hand she had some letters. "Butch!" she said. "What did you do?"

Just then people ran into the headquarters.
They came from the garden next door. All of
them were yelling at once.

"I was just trying to help," said Butch.

"Help!" yelled the owner of the garden.
"You're some help."

At last the people went back to the garden.
Mrs. Stein closed the door. "Butch," she said,
"I'm sorry. Campaign work for an election is
just too much for you. I'll do the letters
myself."

Butch walked home. It was the same old story.
Every time Butch tried to help, something
happened.

PART TWO
Butch Elects a Mayor

School started and Butch forgot about
his father's campaign. Then one day Butch
went downtown. He happened to walk by
election headquarters.

"Hi, Butch," called Mrs. Stein. She came
out. "Will you be at the rally tonight?"

"No," said Butch.

"Oh, do come," said Mrs. Stein. "Your father
will give his big speech tonight. He'll tell what
he plans to do for the city. He has great
plans. A lot of people will be at Spring
Street Hall to hear him. After they hear
his speech, they'll want him for mayor."

That night Spring Street Hall was filled
with people. Butch was there, too.
Mr. Martin came on the stage. He walked
to the microphone. People grew quiet.
Then Mr. Martin began his speech.

"We can't hear you," a man yelled.

Two men ran to the stage. They looked
at the microphone. It wasn't working!

Butch watched. "The microphone plug may not
be plugged in," he thought. He ran to the
wall with the outlets. The microphone was
plugged in. But there were two outlets.
"Could it be that this is not the right
outlet?" Butch took out the plug. He tried
to fit it into the other outlet. The plug
didn't fit. But he tried again and again.
Then it happened.

All the lights went out in the hall.

"Lights!" everyone cried.
"Turn on the lights!"

A man with a light moved to the wall with the outlets. He turned the light on Butch. Butch had the microphone plug in his hand.

"It's all right," he called out. "Some boy was fooling with the plugs."

Mrs. Stein came hurrying over. *"Butch!"* she cried. *"What did you do?"*

"He broke up the rally," said the man. "That's what he did. We'll never get these lights back on tonight."

"What about Mr. Martin's speech?" said Mrs. Stein. "It's the night before the election."

"He can't make a speech in the dark," said the man. "Besides, people are leaving."

The man was right. People were leaving. Soon all of them were gone. The rally was over.

Butch went home with his mother and father.
They did not say a thing to him. When they
got home, Mr. Martin went for a walk.
Mrs. Martin went into the house. Butch
stayed outside. He began to feel sorry
for himself. Butch tried not to cry.

Just then a man came by. He asked Butch,
"Is your father at home?"

"He went for a walk," said Butch.
"What's the matter?" asked the man.

"Everything," said Butch. He told about
the times he had tried to help his father.
He told how his help was never any good.
"And tonight," he said, "no one heard
my father's speech. No one knows
the plans he has for the city. No one
will vote for him. He won't be elected
mayor. And all because I tried to help."

"It's not that bad," said the man. "As for the election, it isn't over. You may find things look much brighter in the morning. Good night." The man walked off. Butch went to bed. He still felt like crying.

The next morning Butch was the first one up. The first thing he did was get the newspaper. He was surprised to see his picture on the first page.

Under the picture he saw,

Butch read the story. It was the story he had told to the man last night. The man wrote for the paper. He wrote the story.

Then Butch saw his father's speech. There it was for everyone to read. Now people would know what Mr. Martin wanted to do for the city. They would vote "Martin for Mayor."

Butch's father read the story. "Now, Butch," he said. "I don't want you to feel bad if I'm not elected."

Butch's mother and father went to vote. Butch went with them. He waited for them to vote. All at once a man shook his hand. He said, "You're the boy I've been reading about! If your father gets elected, it will be because of you." More people came by. They said the same thing to Butch. Butch felt proud. He had helped.

That night Mr. Martin learned that he had won the election.

"I've won," said Butch's father the next morning. "But now I'm a little afraid. It's a lot of work being mayor of this city."

"I'll help you," said Butch.

Mr. and Mrs. Martin looked at each other. This time they didn't say a thing.

The Apple War

Bernice Myers

"They're my apples,"
said King Sam.

"They're on my tree,"
said King Oscar.

"But the apples
fall over
on my land!"
said King Sam.

"The apples
are on
MY tree,
and MY tree
stands on
MY land!"
yelled King Oscar.

"The apples
may be on
your tree,
but they all
FALL
on my land,"
said King Sam.
"So
they are MY APPLES!"

"They're *not!*"
said King Oscar.

"They *are!*"
said King Sam.

"*Not!*"
said King Oscar.

"*Are!*"
said King Sam.
"*Are, are, are!*
This means war.
And I mean
WAR!"

"I'm ready any time,"
said King Oscar.

"How's May 5?
It falls on a Tuesday,"
said King Sam.

"Good,"
said King Oscar.
"I'll see you then."

On the morning of May 4
King Sam called for
William.
"Find out if King Oscar
is ready
for our war.
Tomorrow is May 5!"

"But, King!
You can't have a war
tomorrow.
It's your birthday!"
said William.

79

"You're right.
I forgot!
But I can't call off
a war
at the last minute.
A promise is a promise."

"And, King,"
said William,
"you always have
a party
on your birthday.
We've already asked
everyone to come."

King Sam was upset.
He wanted to keep his promise.
But he didn't know
what
to do.

"I know," he said.
"I'll hide!"

"A king doesn't hide,"
said William.

"Then I'll run away,"
said King Sam.

"A king never runs away,"
said William.

"Then say I'm sick,
or my aunt is sick,
or I broke my leg,"
said King Sam.

William acted as if
he didn't hear.

"William,
William.
What will I do?"
King Sam asked.

"Well,"
said William,
"have the war first
and then
your birthday party.
Or,
have your birthday party
and then the war."

"Great idea," said
King Sam.
"I'll have the party
and then the war.
No. No.
The war and then the party.
Oh, I can't make up my mind
now.
I'm going to sleep.
I can think better
in the morning."

The next day
when King Sam got up,
he began to think.
He walked
around and around.
Sometimes he waved
his arms in the air.
At last
he made up his mind.

"I'll get the war over
quickly
and still have time for my
birthday party."
He jumped on his horse,
and off he went
to the battlefield.

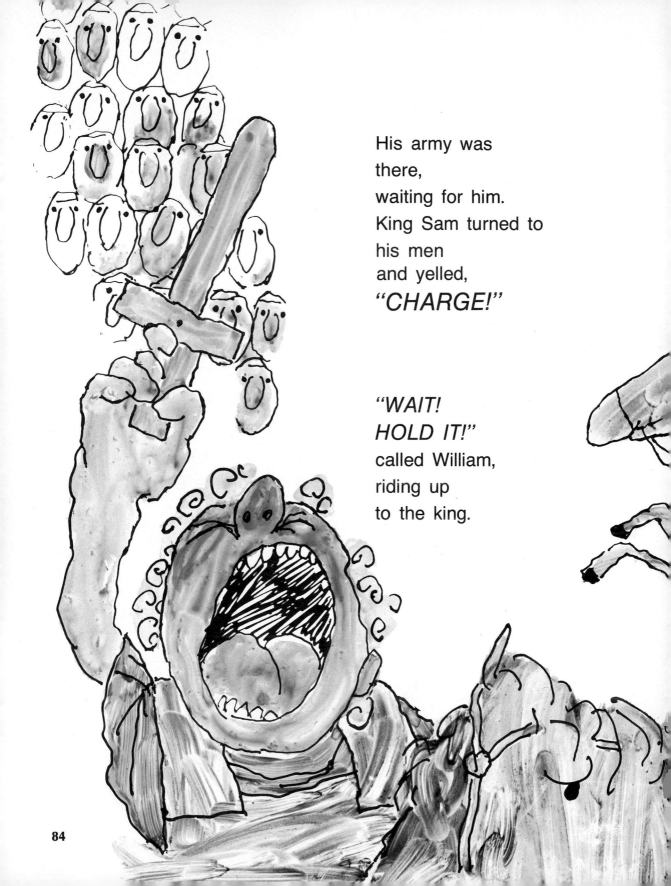

His army was
there,
waiting for him.
King Sam turned to
his men
and yelled,
"CHARGE!"

*"WAIT!
HOLD IT!"*
called William,
riding up
to the king.

"If you have the war
first,
you might not have
anyone at
your party."

"Good thinking,
William,"
said King Sam.

"So we'll have
the party
first
and then the war!"

King Oscar waved
from the other side of
the battlefield.

King Sam waved back.
"We'll fight
this afternoon, Oscar."

"We're going to have
my party first,"
said King Sam.

And right there
in the middle of the
battlefield,
the tables were set,
and everyone began to
eat
and laugh
and sing
and play and . . .

They were having such a
good time
that no one wanted to
fight
anymore.

"You still mad?"
asked King Sam.

"No. You mad?"
asked King Oscar.

"*Me? Mad?*
Why should I be mad?"
asked King Sam.

"Then what were we
going to fight about?"
asked King Oscar.

"I forgot,"
said King Sam.

With that
the two kings
looked at each other
and began to
laugh.

When the army heard
that there would be
no war,
they yelled,
"OH, GOOD!"

"Come see me
sometime,"
said King Sam.
"I'm having a get-together
tomorrow.
Why don't you come
and bring
the family?"

"Thanks.
I will,"
said King Oscar.
"I like your shoes
by the way.
Who's your cobbler?"

"I'll have some
made
for you
if you like,"
said King Sam.

"Here.
Have one of my
apples," said King Oscar.

"*Your* apples?"
said King Sam.

VALENTINE FOR EARTH

To travel to Saturn
Or Venus or Mars,
Or maybe discover
Some uncharted stars.

But do they have anything
Better than we?
Do you think, for instance,
They have a blue sea

For sailing and swimming?
Do planets have hills
With raspberry thickets
Where a song sparrow fills

The summer with music?
And do they have snow
To silver the roads
Where the school buses go?

Oh, I'm all for rockets
And worlds cold or hot,
But I'm wild in love
With the planet we've got!

Read the Ending!

safe + ly = safely
brave + ly = bravely
shy + ly = shyly
quick + ly = quickly

Always play *safely.*
Firefighters work *bravely.*
Ted sang *shyly.*
Mary ran *quickly.*

Which word means *in a shy way?*
Which word means *in a quick way?*
Which word means *in a brave way?*
Which word means *in a safe way?*

What do these words mean?

| slowly | strangely | badly | tightly |

Suffix *ly.* Point out the base words plus endings at the top of the page. Have them read in sentences. Then let the children answer the questions. Help the children use the patterns established above to provide the meanings of the words in the box at the bottom of the page.

THE WATER
ALL AROUND

Until I Saw the Sea

Until I saw the sea
I did not know
that wind
could wrinkle water so.

I never knew
that sun
could splinter a whole sea of blue.

Nor did I know before
a sea breathes in and out upon a shore.

—*Lilian Moore*

Fumio and the Dolphins

Chinoko Nakatani

Fumio lived in a small village by the sea.
When he was not in school, Fumio liked
to fish or swim.

Fumio's father and brother were fishermen.
They caught many kinds of fish. Sometimes
in the fall they caught dolphins. The dolphins
came near the shore to catch fish.

One day Fumio went fishing with his brother,
Taro. They walked by the rocks near
the lighthouse. All at once Fumio saw something
in the sea.

"Taro! Look there! It's the fin of a fish."
The fin came out of the water.
Then a head popped into sight.

"It's a dolphin, Fumio,"
Taro said.

The boys threw a fish to the dolphin.
At once a new head popped up. Fumio cried,
"It's a baby dolphin. The big one is its mother."
     The big dolphin jumped out of the sea.
She caught the fish. Then the baby dolphin
jumped for a fish, too. Fumio threw them
fish, one after the other. Into the air went
the two dolphins.

     Then Taro saw how many fish were gone.
He said, "We must keep the rest. We have
to eat, too. Let's come back tomorrow."
     The next day Fumio could not wait to get
home from school. He ran to the shore.
"The dolphins are coming in," he heard someone
call. All the fishermen ran to their boats.

When he saw the men and the boats going
after the dolphins, Fumio began to worry.
Where were his two special dolphins?
Would they be caught?

Fumio ran to Taro. "I'm afraid that our
dolphins will be caught," he said.

"Don't worry. I'm sure they will stay in back
of the rocks," said Taro. "When the boats
come back, we will go and look for them."

At last the boats came into sight. Fumio saw the fishermen beat the sea. They beat it with long poles. They did this to move the dolphins into the shore. The dolphins swam to the shore. Then the fishermen threw out their nets. They caught the dolphins. Fumio was worried about the baby dolphin and its mother. He was sure they had been caught.

Fumio ran to the nets. He looked at each dolphin in turn. But they all looked alike. Fumio could not find his special friends.

Then Fumio and Taro set out to look for their friends. They took many fish with them.

Fumio hit the side of the boat to call the dolphins, but there was no sign of them. It was starting to grow dark.

At last Taro said, "They must have been caught. Let's go home, Fumio."

But just then they saw two fins cut through the water. "There they are!" called Fumio. "The mother dolphin and her baby are safe after all!"

Fumio threw fish to the two dolphins, and Taro headed the boat out to the open sea.

"We'll lead the dolphins far away, so they will never be caught," said Taro.

The dolphins swam far, far out until they could no longer be seen in the night sea.

Fumio and Taro turned for home.

My Mother Talks to Dolphins

Elizabeth Levy

*My name is Penny, and I'm ten years old. Today
my teacher said we had to write a story called
"What I Want to Be."*

That's not hard for me.

What I Want to Be

I want to be a scientist like my mother.
Mother talks to dolphins. Don't think I'm being
funny. She really is a scientist. And she
really does talk to dolphins. She once lived
with a dolphin because she wanted to teach it
to talk.

Mother says that dolphins seem to talk to
each other just as people do. Maybe you think
that lots of animals talk to each other. Cats
mee-ow. And birds sing. What's so special
about the noises a dolphin makes?

Once Mother saw dolphins do something that cats or birds never do. She saw a sick dolphin whistle to other dolphins for help. The other dolphins came to it. They made noises just as if they were doctors asking the sick dolphin how sick it was. After a lot of noise, the dolphins seemed to come up with a plan. They had to bring food to the sick dolphin. They had to help it get well.

Mother and other scientists thought a lot about the dolphins. Were they talking things over the way people might do if they had to help someone?

Mother says that it will take time to find out if dolphins can talk "people talk." When dolphins are together, they make sounds. Their sounds are not at all like the sounds you or I make. Most of the time dolphins make whistle sounds. They make the sounds through blowholes in their heads.

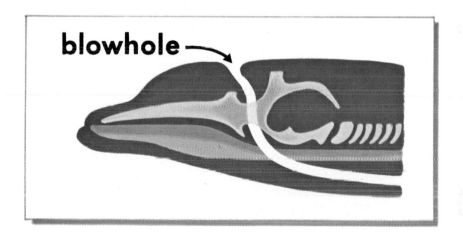

blowhole

But when a dolphin is caught, it will make different sounds. It will try to make sounds like the people around it. Scientists think that the dolphins are trying to talk to them. Maybe the dolphins are asking to be let go. No one knows. But scientists are trying to think of ways to teach dolphins to talk.

One day Mother thought, "Why not teach a dolphin to talk the way we teach babies to talk?" I don't remember my mother teaching me to talk. But she says she did.

Mothers are around their babies a lot. They talk to their babies all the time. Most people like to talk to babies.

A baby is always hearing words. Soon the baby starts to make sounds. The sounds aren't words, but they are like words. This is baby talk. Then the baby gets a little older. And the baby starts to say real words.

Do you know what Mother thinks about dolphins who are caught and try to make "people" sounds? She thinks they are talking baby talk. She thinks that if a dolphin was with people all the time, the dolphin might say real words.

The scientists made a special pool where
Mother and a dolphin lived together. There was
also a room where Mother could cook. And there
was a bed where she could sleep.

My mother went to live in the pool. But I
didn't get to go with her. I went to stay with
my father in Washington. But when I got home,
my mother told me all about it.

Mother and the dolphin played all the time. The dolphin loved to play ball. Every time Mother would throw the ball, she'd say "ball." Soon the dolphin learned to say "ball." The dolphin might have learned other words, but it was hard for my mother to understand the sounds the dolphin made.

Remember, dolphins talk to each other in whistles. It's very hard for them to make any "people" sounds at all through the hole in their heads.

As you can see, I know a lot about dolphins. I find that it helps me in school. If the teacher wants to know what I did last summer, I can tell her about the times my mother let me swim and play with her dolphins.

Or, if we have to write something, I can always write:

"Dolphins in the sea
I wish they'd talk to me . . ."

The only thing is that about the middle of last year, my teacher told me she wanted to hear about something other than dolphins.

But this is the start of a new school year, and I have a new teacher who doesn't know anything about dolphins.

The Shell Collection

Dina Anastasio

PART ONE
Sandy and the Old Man

Every day, when the sand was hot from the morning sun, the boy ran down to the water to play. He loved the mornings. Very few people were on the beach, and he could swim and play by himself.

Sometimes an old man came to the beach and sat near the water. But he was very quiet, and the boy soon forgot that he was there.

After lunch the older children ran down the road and onto the sand, laughing and calling to each other. Then the quiet beach was filled with their noise. The children teased the boy, for he was very small and could not do the things they did.

One day they teased him because he could not swim far out in the water. The boy looked down the beach at the old man. The old man had been watching the children, and he smiled when the boy turned.

The boy walked down the beach to the place where the old man sat in his chair.

"Hello," the boy said as he sat on the sand beside the chair. "My name is Sandy."

"And I'm Bernard," said the old man quietly.

X Every day after that, the boy sat near the old man. As the weeks went by, they became good friends. When the older children teased the boy, the old man smiled and said, "Soon you will be bigger, and you will swim very well. Then the children will not tease you."

X One morning, when the boy came to the beach, the old man handed him an old box. When he opened it, the boy saw a collection of seashells. He picked them up one by one and turned them over and over in his hands. One shell was bright red and very beautiful, and when the boy put it to his ear, he could hear the sea.

"I found this shell far away, on a beach very much like this one," the old man told the boy. "It was many years ago, and I thought it was the most beautiful thing in the world."

Then the man showed the boy the book he had with him that day. It was a book about seashells, and on every page there were beautiful pictures of shells. They found a picture of the red shell, and the old man read its story to the boy.

After that day the boy spent his afternoons looking for shells in the sand. And the older children laughed and yelled far out in the water.

X At first he found only small white shells on
the beach. But as the weeks went by, he began
to find lovely pink, brown, and red shells
for his collection. Whenever he found one,
he took it to Bernard. The old man looked it up
in his book and read to the boy about the new shell.

X For a few weeks the old man told the boy where
to look for the shells. But as the collection grew,
the boy came to know where they were. Then he
no longer needed help.

A Shell for Sandy

One day, while the boy walked slowly along
the hot sand looking for shells, he kicked over
a big black stone. There, where the stone had been,
lay the most beautiful pink shell that the boy had
ever seen. He picked it up and ran down
the beach to his friend.

Bernard turned the shell over and over
in his hand. Then he picked up his shell book
and looked through the pages very quickly until
he found the one he wanted. He showed the page
to the boy, and they looked at it together.
There were many shells much like Sandy's,
but not one was just like it. Slowly they went
through every page of the shell book.

X "I think," said Bernard happily, "that you have
found a very special and new shell. As you
can see, there are many like it in the book, but not
one is just like yours. But to be sure, we
will go to the museum this afternoon and look
at the collection of shells there. Then, if we don't
find one like yours, we will show it
to the scientist at the museum. He will tell us
if you have found a new shell."

After lunch the boy ran down to the beach
to meet the old man, and together they walked
into town. When they got to the museum, they
asked to see the shell collection. A woman led them
into a room with cases and cases of shells.
The old man and the boy walked slowly
around the room and looked at every shell.
But they could not find the boy's shell,
and so they asked to see the scientist.

When the boy showed him his shell,
the scientist said, "I have never
seen a shell just like this. It could be
a new kind of shell that no one
has ever found before. Where did you find it?"

"Under a black stone on the beach,"
said Sandy.

"Will you show me?" asked the scientist.

The old man and the boy led the scientist down
to the beach, and the boy showed him the black
stone. "That's where I first saw the shell,"
said the boy.

The older children walked behind the scientist
while he looked through the sand. When they asked
him what he was doing, he told them about
the boy's new shell.

"If Sandy has really found a new kind of shell,"
the scientist said, "he can name it whatever he
wishes."

After a few weeks the scientist called the boy and said, "It looks as if you have really found a special shell. Come to the museum when you have thought of a name for it."

That night the boy could not sleep. He lay in his bed thinking of names for his shell. But he was not happy with any of them. When at last he fell asleep, he still had not made up his mind what to name his shell.

X The noon sun was hot in the sky when the boy got to the beach the next day. But the old man was not yet there. While the boy waited for his friend, he lay on the sand. The older children stopped to say hello and to ask about his shell.

"What do you think I
should name my shell?"
the boy asked.

X "Name it *Bobby*," laughed
a boy named Bobby.
"That's a good name."

"Name it *Peter*,"
said his brother.

"No, no, name it *Ed!*"
called Ed.

"How about *George?*"
yelled a boy named George.

But Sandy didn't like any of the names the older children thought of.

All at once the boy jumped quickly to his feet and ran down the beach to wait for the old man. He had thought of a wonderful name for his shell. When he saw his friend walking slowly near the water, he ran to meet him. He asked the old man to go with him to the museum to see the scientist. Together they walked up the beach and into the town.

At the museum the boy saw the scientist. "I would like to name my shell after Bernard," he said, "because Bernard is my friend."

"That is a good name," said the scientist. "The shell will be called

Conus bernardi."

The old man smiled
and took the boy's hand,
and together they walked
back to the sea.

The Collector

I have a collection
Of bottles and sticks,
Of seashells and small bells
And baubles and bricks,

Of spiders and gliders
And crayons and cans,
Of kite string and fly wings
And red rubber bands.

Hangers and twangers
And wires that connect
Are some more of the things
That I like to collect.

—Marci Ridlon

124

Signal Words

Some words are like signals. They tell you that something is coming. The words in red below usually tell you that more words are coming.

The boy went to the museum.

The girl ran down the beach.

The dolphins jumped into the air.

The helicopter flew over the town.

The boy looked at the moon.

I found this shell on the beach.

Here are some more signal words. Can you use them in sentences?

up	by	before	above	under
from	with	inside	behind	through

Phrase Markers. Have the paragraph and the sentences below it read. Let the children make up sentences using the prepositions listed. Write their sentences on the board, underlining the prepositional phrases. When all the sentences are on the board, have just the phrases read so the children will get the feeling of a phrase and its function.

Hurray for Captain Jane!

Sam Reavin

PART ONE
A Sailor's Hat

Jane went to a party and came home with three prizes. Her little brother Simon met her at the door.

"What do you have, Jane?" he asked.

"Prizes," Jane said. She looked very proud. "I won them at the party."

"Open them! Open them!" said Simon. "Let's see what's inside."

Jane opened the little prize first. It was a box of jelly beans. She showed Simon the prize.

"I like that prize," said Simon. "Can I have all the black ones?"

"No," Jane said. "I like the black ones, too."

She opened another prize. It was a hat made
of folded paper. She showed the hat to Simon.

"A sailor's hat!" said Simon. "Can I have it?"

"No, I like it, too," said Jane, and she put
the sailor's hat on.

The last prize was a cake of soap with the name
BOBBING BEAUTY on it. The soap had a nice smell.

"Soap!" cried Simon. "What a funny prize!"

But Jane liked all the prizes. She ate the jelly beans and smelled the soap. She put on the hat for the rest of the day.

She still had the hat on when she took her bath that night.

She took BOBBING BEAUTY into the bath, too.

"It floats!" she thought happily. She tried to make the soap stay under the water. But it kept bobbing right up again. She couldn't keep it in her hands.

Jane reached over to pick up BOBBING BEAUTY, and her hat fell into the water. She was about to put it on again, when she saw something.

"That hat floats like a little ship," she thought. "I'll make it go faster."

Jane got way down into the tub. Then she kicked her feet and made little waves. The ship began to move over the waves faster and faster. As it came closer, it looked bigger and bigger.

All at once the water in the tub became a great ocean.

Everywhere she looked, Jane saw water. She knew she was standing on the top deck of an ocean liner.

Jane looked down on the main deck. Everywhere there were children. Boys and girls were laughing. They were running and playing tag. Even way up on the top deck she could hear them.

A sailor was standing at the wheel. Jane was glad there was someone to talk to.

"What's your name?" she asked the sailor at the wheel.

"Kate, Sailor First Class," the girl said.

"My name is Jane," said Jane.

"Aye, aye, Captain," said Kate, Sailor First Class.

Captain! Jane looked around. "Oh, I'm the captain of this ship," she thought. "I'd better get to work."

Just then, a sailor came up to her. He looked just like her brother Simon. The sailor saluted and stood at attention.

"Can I help you, Captain?" he asked.

After some thought, Jane said, "Please bring me some black jelly beans."

"Aye, aye, Captain," said the sailor. "Black jelly beans. At once!"

The sailor came back with the jelly beans.

"Ask the first mate to come to the top deck," Jane said to the sailor.

The first mate came right away. He saluted and stood at attention.

"Please keep watch here," Jane said to the first mate. "I wish to look my ship over. I think I'll start with the engine room."

Jane went to the engine room. Everyone saluted her and stood at attention as she went by.

From the engine room, she went to the main deck. She stopped to talk to the children. She gave them all black jelly beans.

"Captain," said one of the children, "may I take your picture?"

"Well," said Jane, "I haven't the time right now."

"Please!" said the boy. "I'd like to have a picture of the captain of an ocean liner."

The boy was just about to take the picture, when a voice came over the loudspeaker.

"Captain! You are needed on the top deck!"

The Iceberg

Jane ran back to the top deck. The first mate was looking out over the ocean with his spyglass. He looked worried.

"Captain," he said. "There is an iceberg right ahead of us."

Jane picked up a spyglass and looked at the iceberg. For a minute, she thought she had seen something like it before.

"It's almost as big as our ship!" cried the first mate. "And we're headed right for it. Don't you want to change course, Captain?"

"No," Jane said slowly. "No change. Stay on course. I want to get a closer look."

The children on the main deck grew very quiet. They stopped running and playing, and stood waiting.

"There's an iceberg right ahead," they said to one another.

The ship was moving closer and closer to the iceberg. Soon Jane could read the words BOBBING BEAUTY.

She gave a strange order. "Ready the fire hoses!"

"Ready all fire hoses!" said the first mate over the loudspeaker.

Jane gave another order. "Cut the engines!" she said.

The engines stopped, and the ship began to slow down. They were almost to the iceberg. They were sure to hit it now.

"Turn the hoses on the iceberg!" was Jane's next order. All hoses on the ocean liner were turned on the iceberg.

Then, to the great surprise of everyone but Jane, the iceberg began to melt and move to the side. At the same time, clouds of giant bright bubbles went up into the air.

The ship was safe!

Jane gave another order. "Turn on the engines!" she said.

As the ship moved, the bubbles fell onto the main deck. The children ran after the big bubbles. They laughed as they threw them to one another.

"Hurray for Captain Jane!" they cried. "Hurray!"

Jane smiled to herself as she heard the cries of "Hurray." But it was time to look over the ship again and change course.

She was happy that everything was in order.

"I like to run a tight ship," she told the first mate. Then she saw something she hadn't seen before. It was a shiny handle next to the wheel.

"What's this?" she said. She turned the shiny handle to the right.

All at once there was a loud, strange sound. Then the ocean was gone.

Jane found herself sitting in an empty tub.
At her side was the cake of soap and the
paper hat.

There was not much left of the soap. Jane
tried to put the hat on. But it fell apart
in her hands. No matter how hard she tried,
she could not make it into a sailor's hat again.

To her surprise, the hat now looked just
like a pilot's cap.

"Oh," said Jane. "Maybe next time I'll be
the captain of a jet plane."

Undersea

Beneath the waters
  Green and cool
The mermaids keep
  A swimming school.

The oysters trot;
  The lobsters prance;
The dolphins come
  To join the dance.

But the jellyfish
  Who are rather small,
Can't seem to learn
  The steps at all.

—*Marchette Chute*

139

The Last Blue Whale

George McCue

Ben Blue Whale is alone. Each day he swims a long way looking for another blue whale. He looks in all parts of the oceans. There he sees other kinds of whales. But he never sees a blue whale like himself.

Ben has been looking for blue whales since his mother left him. He was small then. Still he remembers that day. Ben and his mother had heard the noise of a boat. But before they could swim away, there had been another loud noise. It had been made by men on the boat. The men had killed Ben's mother.

Ben did not understand what had happened. He didn't know what men or boats were. All he knew was that his mother had left him.

   Ben missed his mother. She had taken
good care of him since the day he was born.
Like all whales, Ben was born under the water.
As soon as he was born, his mother put her head
under him. She helped him to the top of the
water. He had to get air. Whales are like
people and land animals in that they must have air
to live.

Ben's mother fed him her milk. He needed
lots of milk each day. It helped him grow
and keep warm. Ben did not have hair
to keep him warm, and the ocean was cold.
His mother's milk made Ben fat. And the fat
helped him stay warm.

Ben's mother never let other animals hurt him.
Many times hungry killer whales tried to kill Ben.
They would hurt his mother. But she wouldn't
let them hurt Ben.

Sometimes Ben's mother sang when she was
with him. She didn't sing the way people do.
You might not think she sang very well. But
Ben loved to hear his mother sing. When she
sang, it told him she was near. And when his
mother was near, Ben was safe and happy.

Since Ben's mother was gone, Ben was alone
in the ocean. But he was lucky. Now he was big,
and he could take care of himself. Now he
didn't need his mother's milk. He could eat
food that he found in the ocean. To Ben
the ocean was like one big bowl of soup.

Ben grew and grew. Then one day he was
a big blue whale. He didn't know it, but he
was the biggest animal in the world. Ben was
100 feet long.

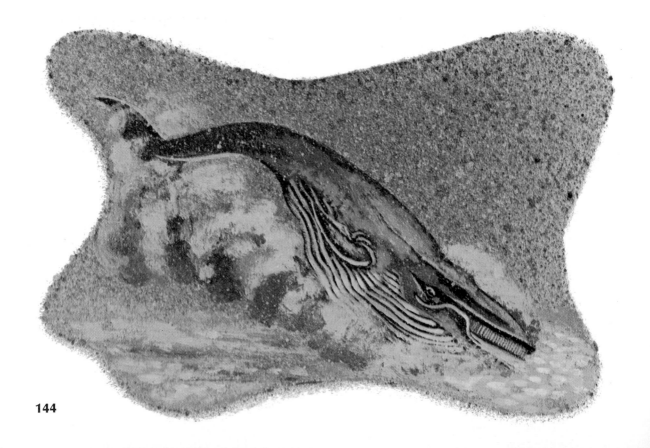

Now Ben is older. And he gets more lonely
each day. He wants to find another blue whale.
But he never sees a blue whale. Men have killed
most of them. Ben is one of the last blue whales
left in the world.

Secrets of the Sea

The sea is a familiar home to many plants and animals. But to people who live on land, the sea is a place filled with secrets.

Unlocking the secrets of the sea is the job of both of these women. One is a *marine biologist.* She studies the plants and animals that live in the sea. The other woman is an *aquanaut.* For part of each year, she lives in a special underwater laboratory. From her underwater home, she can easily go out and explore the sea around her.

These men, too, know that the sea has many secrets. One man is a *sponge diver.* He often stays underwater for hours, collecting sponges. His special diving suit helps him to breathe. The other man is a *lobster fisherman.* But he does not use a rod and reel. Instead, he uses a special trap called a lobster pot. The lobsters that he catches will be food for people.

Would you like a job that brings you close to the sea? Would you like to help unlock its secrets?

A Home in the Desert

Olga Economakis

PART ONE

No Water

Abu's home was the desert, all of the desert. Abu did not live in a house in one place like most children. He lived with his mother and father in a tent. Their tent moved with them. And their animals moved with them. They moved to look for grass and water. From place to place in the desert they went. Each new place was like the one they just left. And no place even had a name.

In summer the hot sun dried up the springs. The grass did not grow. As Abu's father put up the tent, he would say, "Tomorrow we will move on. We may find grass ahead for the animals." So just about every day they would pack up their things and move to a new place.

Once Abu's father told him a story about the ocean. "Is the desert like the ocean?" Abu asked.

"Yes, my child," said his father. "In many ways the desert is like the ocean. But it has sand in place of water."

Abu liked to think of the desert as an ocean. He would ride on his camel. But he would pretend that he was on a boat. And he would be looking for an island. He wanted to find a big, green island. He wanted an island that he could name.

Most of the time Abu was happy. Mornings he liked to watch the sun come up. It came right out of the sand like a ball. And at night he liked to hear the sounds of his mother and father as they talked.

Some nights the sides of the tent were up
to let in the air. Then Abu would look at
the stars in the sky. And he would pretend
that each star was a sheep. He would watch
the sheep until he fell asleep. Then Mother
would come and cover him up.

Other times Abu would pretend that each star
was a drop of water. "If we had all that water,"
he would say, "we would never have to move again.
Our tent would be a real home. Mother wouldn't
have to keep packing our things. And Father
could have a real chair to sit on."

But Abu's father would just laugh. He would
say, "We don't have a drop of that water. When
the summer comes, the water dries up. Most of
the grass dries up, too. And animals can't go
without grass and water. We must move on."

Then Abu would stop pretending. He knew
that this place was not an island that he could
name. It was just another too-dry place. They
would have to pull up the tent poles again.
They would have to go into the big desert that
he had to call home.

Oasis of the Stars

One day Abu asked if he could dig into the earth. He wanted to see where the water went.

"I want to try to find my shimmering stars," Abu said. "I want to find my small drops of water. I think if I dig long enough and deep enough, I may find them."

"Dig for stars?" his father laughed. "Child, there is nothing under the sand but more sand. The stars are above the sand. We must move on."

But Abu asked once more, "Please, Father. May I just try?"

His father smiled. "Well, you may look," he said. "But when our spring runs dry, we must be on our way."

That same night Abu began to dig. He found
a place where it seemed that the grass was
greener than any other place. There he dug.

Night after night he dug. After a while,
his hole was so deep that he stood in it up to
his knees. But there was no water.

It was hard work. At times the sand fell back
into the hole. Then Abu had to make a wall of
rocks to hold the sand back. He found the rocks
in the hard-packed earth under the sand.
Sometimes he had to dig with his hands
to pull out a big rock.

Deeper and deeper Abu dug. Then just his head could be seen above the hole. But still there was no water.

At times Abu gave up the hard work. He did not dig in the hole. Then he would look up at the night sky. He would look at the stars that were shimmering all over it. They looked like little drops of water. After that, Abu would dig some more. But Abu's water stayed in the sky. His small hole in the big desert got deeper. It was now above his head. And still there was no water.

Sometimes Abu's father would come and look
into the hole. "Abu, have you found them yet,
your shimmering stars? Well, never mind.
Summer is coming. We will find water
in some other place."

Then one day while Abu worked, his father
came to him to say that the spring had
run dry. They would leave the next morning.

Abu cried that night as he dug deeper into
the hole. If only his tears could help.
But tears were not enough. They could never
fill up a hole so deep. "I will never
find stars in the earth," he thought. The stars
were in the sky. The earth was only desert.

As Abu climbed to the top of the hole, he could feel something cool. "The earth is cool," said Abu. "It feels damp. But it is only my tears." Then he picked up some dirt from another part of the hole. "It feels different," he thought.

"*Father*, please come!" he cried. "The earth is damp. There must be water under here."

Abu's father was sitting outside the tent. He didn't get up but smiled and said, "It feels that way because the night air makes the earth cool. Come, child, stop your digging, and sit with me. I will tell you about the ocean. You like that story."

But Abu went on digging. He couldn't see
out of the hole now. To carry the dirt out
he had to climb up little stairs he had made
in the side of the hole. At last he fell asleep,
and his father had to carry him into the tent.
As he put Abu to bed, he smiled. "The child
has dreams, and sometimes dreams hurt.
But dreams, like water and food, make boys
grow into men."

The next day the camels were packed.
Abu went to take a last look at the hole
he had made. He looked at his rock wall.
Then his eyes went down the stairs
he had made. At last he was looking
at the bottom of the hole. At the bottom
the sand was darker than it had been. He took
off his shoes and started down the stairs.

Deeper and deeper he went until he reached
the bottom of the hole, and his feet could feel
wet sand. He got down on his knees to feel it
with his hands. It was wet. It was really wet!

"Please, Father, come quickly," he cried.
"The water is here. *It's here!*"

Abu's father looked at Abu on his knees
at the bottom of the hole. Then he climbed
into the hole and picked up some sand.
It was wet. "My child, you were right,"
he said. "Your shimmering stars were there
under the sand. We will stay here."

So Abu and his father made the hole
into a well.

Now their tent is a real home with a real chair for his father. And his mother doesn't have to keep packing their things.

And now when the sun goes down and night falls on the desert, Abu looks into his well and sees his shimmering stars. He has named the place he lives Oasis of the Stars.

The Waters of the Earth

PHOTOGRAPH, ERICH LESSING, MAGNUM

Noah Releasing the Dove

ARTIST UNKNOWN

Many artists have chosen water as a subject for their work. One artist showed Noah in the ark. He made the picture by fitting together bits of brightly colored glass. Such pictures are called mosaics.

162

Fishing Boat

INGBET

This is a photograph of a fishing boat resting safely in the harbor after a day at sea. The soft colors help to give us a quiet feeling.

Sailing Ship

HOLDEN WEINTRAUB

A boy in the second grade made this crayon drawing of a sailing ship. Crayon drawings may be seen in many fine museums.

Venice

LOREN MacIVER

Here are three different views of Venice, an old seaport, famous for its beautiful harbor and canals. One shows a city of bright colors and interesting shapes. Another is a lifelike painting of the Grand Canal. A third is a woodcut of the harbor.

The Grand Canal

CANALETTO

Bird's-eye View of Venice

JACOPO DE' BARBARI

Toilers of the Sea

ALBERT PINKHAM RYDER

In this painting the fishermen's boat seems to be part of the sea. It glides along beneath a partly darkened sky, the sun lighting its way.

Amida, or Buddha Falls, Kiso

KATSUSHIKA HOKUSAI

The artist who made this woodcut of a waterfall didn't try to make it look real. He showed us a beautiful arrangement of shapes and colors.

Sea and Rain

JAMES McNEILL WHISTLER

In this painting the artist used bands of soft colors. The blue-green sea gives us the peaceful feeling of walking alone on a rainy day.

168

Way Down Deep

Underneath the water
Way down deep
In sand and stones and seaweed
Starfish creep
Snails inch slowly
Oysters sleep
Underneath the water
Way down deep.

—Mary Ann Hoberman

THE SKY ABOVE

February Twilight

I stood beside a hill
   Smooth with new-laid snow,
A single star looked out
   From the cold evening glow.

There was no other creature
   That saw what I could see —
I stood and watched the evening star
   As long as it watched me.

                 —*Sara Teasdale*

Barbara Brenner

The Flying Patchwork Quilt

PART ONE
The Old Chest

If it weren't for Mother, it would never have
happened. You see, Mother collects stuff,
and she keeps the stuff around the house.

One day Mother came home with an old chest.
"It'll be a great place to store winter clothes,"
she told Father. "And look what's in it."

"What is it?" asked Father. He doesn't like
old stuff the way Mother does.

"It's an old patchwork quilt," Mother said.
"Isn't it beautiful? It'll be nice to have."

"It's nice," Father said. "But what are you
going to do with it?"

"It'll come in handy," Mother said. That's
what she always says when she doesn't know
what to do with some old thing. She folded
the quilt. Then she put the folded quilt
into the chest.

173

That was the last I saw of the patchwork
quilt for a long time. It lay at the bottom
of the old chest. When spring came, it got
covered with winter clothes.

Then one day I saw the quilt again. It
was all because of my sister Ellen. Ellen
was just five. And she was always going
through a stage. At that time she was going
through the stage where she wanted to fly.
She tried everything. I told her that she
couldn't fly. But she kept on trying.

Well, one day Ellen and I were outside. Then
Mother came out. "Carl," she said to me.
"I have to go to the store. Will you
keep an eye on Ellen?"

"Sure," I said. "Don't worry about a thing."
So Mother went off down the street.

I was working on a bird house. So I was
really keeping more of an ear on Ellen than
an eye. You see, Ellen talks to herself. I
thought that as long as I could hear her
talking, she was all right.

She started to play her flying game. She
was standing on the stairs with a balloon
tied around her. I watched her jump and land
right on the balloon. It broke with a pop!

I began to feel a little sorry for her.
"Ellen," I called to her, "it won't work. You
have to wave your arms if you're going to fly."

"It will so work," Ellen said. "I just haven't
found the right flying thing yet. You'll see."
And with that, she ran off into the apartment.

A few minutes after that I looked up and there
was Ellen. She was about to try flying with the
old patchwork quilt. "No, you don't," I yelled.
"That's Mother's."

"Please, Carl. Just this once. I'll put it
right back," she said. "I just want to try it."

"All right," I said. "But promise that after you
fall with the silly thing you will stop playing
this game for the rest of the afternoon!"

She promised. I helped her pin it on, and I gave her a hand up onto the stairs again. "Don't forget to wave your arms," I said.

Ellen yelled,
"One,

two,

three."

"Jump," I said.

She did. Now, I'm not making this up. One minute she was jumping off the stairs. And the next minute she was floating over my head. *Flying*! Laughing and flying all over the place.

"I told you, I told you!" she yelled. *"I knew the patchwork quilt was the right thing."*

I just stood there with my mouth open. A little wind came along, and she floated up higher. She began to look a little afraid.

"Carl?" she called, kind of funny.
I reached for her leg and missed.

The wind took Ellen higher and higher. Before I knew it, she was flying over the treetops.

"Don't worry. I'm coming," I yelled. I ran down the street after her. I stopped when I got to the corner. There was no sign of Ellen. Everything was just the way it always is at the corner.

Mr. Peters was sitting next to his newspaper stand. "Mr. Peters! Mr. Peters," I called. "Did you see Ellen fly by just now?"

"In a balloon or a jet?" Mr. Peters laughed.

I did not think that was funny. "It was a patchwork . . . Oh, never mind," I said.

"Sorry, Carl," said Mr. Peters. "I haven't seen her. But if she lands around here, I'll let you know."

The Missing Quilt

I ran up and down the streets. As I ran,
I tried to look up at the sky at the same time.
When I got to the library, I saw Ellen.
She was caught on top of the library flagpole.
Boy, was it good to see her!

I ran into the library. I looked for someone to help me. **"Mrs. Bright,"** I called.

Mrs. Bright hurried over. "Shhhhhhhh," she said.

"But Mrs. Bright, my sister is outside on the flagpole, and . . ."

"Well, tell her to get off, dear. We don't like children to climb on the flagpole."

"You don't understand!"

"Shhhhhhhh."

"I can't help it. My sister needs help now!"

"Whatever are you talking about, Carl?"

"My sister has been flying all over the city. Now she's caught on top of the flagpole."

"What!
Carl, are you making this up?"

I looked her right in the eye and said,
"No, Mrs. Bright. And please hurry."

We ran out of the library and looked up at the top
of the flagpole. But Ellen was not there.

I looked at Mrs. Bright, and she looked at me.
What could I say? She'd never believe me now.
So I just walked away.

"Well, let's face it," I said to myself. "Your sister is gone. No one will help you find her because no one will believe you."

I thought about going to the police. I would say, "You see, my sister flew away. She was wearing a patchwork quilt." What a horrible thought!

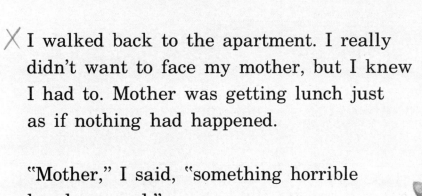

X I walked back to the apartment. I really
didn't want to face my mother, but I knew
I had to. Mother was getting lunch just
as if nothing had happened.

"Mother," I said, "something horrible
has happened."

X "What?" asked my mother. "Where?"

"Right here. But I couldn't help it,"
I said.

"I'm sure you couldn't," said my mother.
"But tell me about it."

"It's Ellen," I began.

"Yes," Mother said. "I told you to keep an eye on her, but when I came home you were gone."

"I tried to watch her, but I couldn't keep up with her," I said.

Mother smiled. How could she at a time like this?

"Now, come on, Carl. She's been standing there by that tree ever since I left," Mother said.

"What tree? Where?" I asked.

I ran to the window. I could hardly believe my eyes. But sure enough, there was Ellen. She was standing by the tree, talking to herself.

I ran out to her. I tried to keep myself from doing something silly like kissing her. "*Where have you been?*" I yelled.

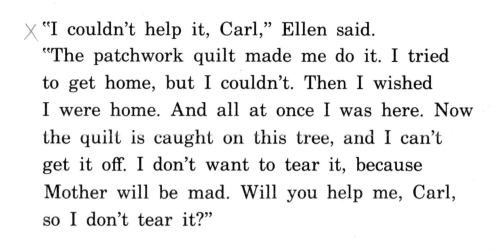

"I couldn't help it, Carl," Ellen said.
"The patchwork quilt made me do it. I tried
to get home, but I couldn't. Then I wished
I were home. And all at once I was here. Now
the quilt is caught on this tree, and I can't
get it off. I don't want to tear it, because
Mother will be mad. Will you help me, Carl,
so I don't tear it?"

Now that Ellen was safe, I started to think
about that quilt. Someone could fly with it on.
I thought about flying to see Grandmother
at the beach or my aunt at the farm. But Ellen
put a stop to my dreams.

"Carl, please help me," she said.
"I don't want to tear the quilt."

185

Ellen was right. The quilt was caught. While
I helped her free it, I said, "Now remember.
We won't say a word about this to Mother.
She doesn't even know we have the quilt.
I'll put it back in the chest."

I got it into the apartment without Mother
seeing it. But as I was putting it in the
chest, I thought, "Why wait? Why not take
a ride tonight?" So I put the quilt in my room.

That night I got all set for the takeoff.
Everyone went to bed. Then I opened
the window. I looked up into the dark sky.
There was a moon. That would help. I picked
up the quilt to pin it on.

"Well, here goes!" I said. Then I
dropped the pin. I put the quilt down to get
another pin, and then it happened. The wind
caught the quilt. I saw it take off. It went
flying out the window. I reached for it, but
I missed it. In two minutes it was out of sight.

We never saw the patchwork quilt again.
I'd think I dreamed it all if it weren't
for Ellen. She remembers it all. Mother
remembers, too, in a way. Every once
in a while she says, "I wonder what became
of that quilt that was in the chest?"

Then Ellen gives me a look. She seems to say,
"Why don't we tell her?"

But I don't want to. No one would believe us.

Ellen's out of her flying stage now. But I
still think about flying a lot.

The other day Mother came home with an old rug.
It looks just like any other rug. But if someone
were to take that rug to the top of the stairs
and sit in the middle of it . . .

Well, who knows?

190

I Can Fly

I can fly, of course,
Very low,
Not fast,
Rather slow.
I spread my arms
Like wings,
Lean on the wind,
And my body zings
About.
Nothing showy—
A few loops
And turns—
But for the most
Part,
I just coast.
However,
Since people are prone
To talk about
It,
I generally prefer,
Unless I am alone,
Just to walk about.

—Felice Holman

Dina Anastasio

The Race

PART ONE
Jenny's Pigeon

Pete was Jenny's pigeon. And this was the morning of his first race.

Last night Jenny had taken Pete to the place where the race would begin. When she had left him, she had been happy. She could not wait for the race to begin. But now Jenny was not happy. She was not sure that she wanted Pete in the race.

Jenny had spent many days teaching her pigeon to find his way home. She knew that he did it very well. But she also knew that things do happen to pigeons as they fly home. Sometimes they don't come back at all. What if there were rain or snow? Could Pete find his way home in snow?

"It's Pete's first race," she thought. "Anything could happen. But I'm just being silly," she told herself. "Pete's big and fast. He's been far away from home before. And he's always come back."

Jenny was very worried. She did not want the race to begin. Then she looked at the clock. "I can't do anything now," she thought.

Jenny took the stairs to the roof two at a time. She pulled open the door and ran out. Then she sat down on the roof.

Jenny tried to picture what Pete was doing. Soon someone would open his cage. Pete would fly out into the bright sky.

At ten Jenny heard the telephone ring. Then her mother climbed up to the roof to tell her that Pete had been set free. He had started the race. He had started the long trip home.

Jenny sat still on the hot roof. The roof grew hotter and hotter. She watched the ant-like people on the street below. But no one below could take her mind off Pete. Now and then she looked at the sky to see if she could see him.

When Jenny heard the noon whistle, she became afraid. Pete never took this long to fly this far. Jenny just knew something had happened.

Jenny's mother came up to the roof. "Lunch is ready," she said.

Jenny looked out at the clear summer sky. "He'll never come back," she said. "Will he, Mother?"

"Pete's always come back before," her mother said. "I'm sure he'll be back soon. Pigeons can fly in rain and snow. They can fly even when they're sick or hungry. That's why pigeons carried messages in the war."

"*Messages?*" asked Jenny. "How did they do that?"

"The messages were tied to their legs," said Jenny's mother. "They flew the messages from the battlefields back to headquarters. Sometimes they were days late, but most of them made it. And so will Pete."

Jenny was not so sure. "What if Pete missed our roof and landed on a different one? Or what if he ran into something and was too badly hurt to fly all the way home?" she thought.

Jenny knew that it was too late for Pete to win the race. But she didn't care about that now. She just wanted him back.

"I don't think I'll have any lunch," she told her mother. And she turned back to watch the sky. When she saw no sign of Pete, she looked down at the street below.

Jenny's mother went downstairs. Soon she came back with a small chair. And she had two sandwiches. She placed them near Jenny. Then she went back to their small apartment.

After a while Jenny's mother went up to the roof again. Now Jenny was sitting in the chair. But the sandwiches were just where she had put them. So she took them back downstairs. She left Jenny alone to wait for Pete.

The Long Wait

Jenny's father came home from work. Jenny was still on the roof. The sky was getting dark.

Jenny heard her father behind her. "Pete didn't come home," she said.

"I know," he said. He sat down beside her. To take her mind off Pete, he began to tell her a story. It was about some brave pigeons. He told how they carried messages in the war.

But Jenny didn't care about other pigeons. She cared only about Pete. Was he lost? Was he hungry? Could he find his way home in the dark? Jenny felt sad.

As Jenny's father told his story, the sky
became darker and darker. Jenny moved closer
to her father. She felt so sad that soon
she began to cry.

"I guess you don't care much about other birds
when Pete is lost, do you?" her father asked.
"I'm sorry. I should have told you another
kind of story. Would you like it if I just
sat here with you? We don't have to talk at all
if you don't want to."

So Jenny's father stayed there with her on the
roof. And together they waited for Pete.

Jenny was watching the street below light up
for the night when she heard her father say,
"Jenny! Jenny, look!" Quickly he pulled her to
her feet and showed her a small dot in the sky.

Carefully they watched as the dot moved
closer and closer. At last they were sure.
The dot was Pete. He wasn't lost!

Jenny ran to the other side of the roof.
She waited for Pete to land. He was flying very
slowly. Jenny was afraid that he was hurt.
At last he flew close enough for Jenny to reach
him. She took him in her arms. Then she carried
him into the light. She felt his legs and looked
at him carefully. Only then was she sure that he
was not hurt.

"He came back. He came back," she said over and over to her father. Then she got Pete some food and water. And she put him carefully into his box.

"Where did you go?" she asked as she closed the top of the box. "What happened to you?"

But Jenny felt sure that she would never know what had happened to Pete. And she really didn't care. Pete was home!

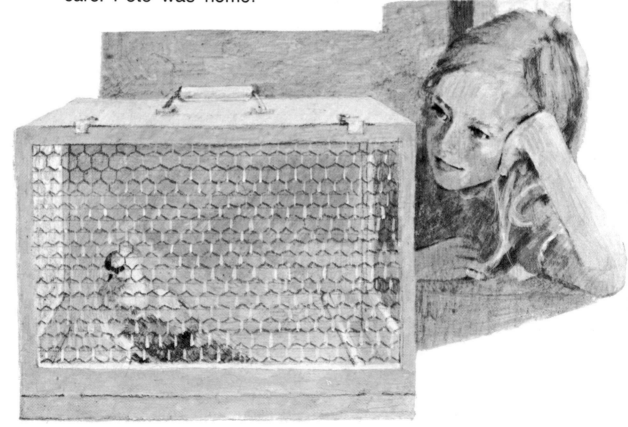

More Signal Words

The words in red are signal words. They tell you that more words are coming.

Butch was sad as he walked home.
Ben could eat the food that he found.
Jenny looked up when she heard her father.
We were quiet while the band played.
I haven't seen her since we got here.
We ran until we got home.

Here are some more signal words. Can you use them in sentences?

because   who   wherever   whenever

Phyllis LaFarge

Granny's Fish Story

Swamp Halibut and Bush Mackerel

Julie ran to the phone. It was Granny.
"How about coming to see me?" Granny asked.
"When?" asked Julie.
"I'll pick you up tomorrow," said Granny.
"It will be for overnight and the next day.
Bring a friend if you like."

Bringing a friend would make a trip to Granny's
lots of fun. And so Julie asked Sarah. Granny
lived in the country. Julie knew Sarah had never
been to the country before.

"What's your grandmother like?" Sarah asked
Julie. They were waiting at Julie's house for
Granny the next afternoon.

"She wears blue jeans and sneakers," said
Julie. "And she lives in the woods. She knows
a lot about animals."

"She doesn't sound like other grandmothers," said Sarah.

"She isn't," said Julie.

Julie didn't know if Sarah would like Granny. Maybe she should have asked another friend.

Then they heard Granny's car. Granny came in, wearing jeans and sneakers. She looked just as Julie had said.

"I'll come up and bring you back tomorrow, girls," Mother said. "Have a good time."

It took about an hour to get to Granny's. At last Granny turned off the big road. She went down the dirt road that led to her house.

"Is this a real road?" asked Sarah. Julie thought Sarah sounded a little surprised.

Granny laughed. "No, it isn't," she said. "I lived on a real road for years. It had cars and trucks going by all the time. Then I made up my mind that I was going to live by a dirt road in the woods."

"What kind of animals live in the woods?" Sarah asked. She was looking out the car window into the trees.

"Oh, swamp halibut," said Granny, "and bush mackerel."

"I've never heard of them," said Sarah. Now she really did sound surprised.

"That's a joke," said Julie. "There's no such thing as a swamp halibut or a bush mackerel."

But Julie didn't laugh out loud. She remembered that only a few years before, she herself had thought there were such things.

Soon they were at Granny's. They saw Trev, Granny's puppy, in his doghouse. Down the hill from Granny's house was a pond.

"Can we go wading?" asked Sarah.

"Sure," said Granny.

"We can look for frogs, too," said Julie.

Sarah and Julie spent the afternoon by the pond. They found small frogs and put them into boxes. They walked around the pond. They looked for big frogs. Sometimes the frogs floated out into the pond. Only their eyes showed above the water.

Trev liked to hunt frogs, too. His tail wagged every time he was near one. But most of the time, the frog jumped away just as he reached for it.

Julie caught a big frog. Sarah asked
to hold it. She held it for a minute.
Then, she let it go.

Soon Granny came to tell them it was time
to eat. "Looks like a thunderstorm," Granny said.

Julie and Sarah had not noticed the dark
clouds in the sky.

After eating, the girls played. Then Granny read them a story. But the girls didn't really hear the story. They were looking out the window at the lightning in the dark sky.

"Are we really going to have a thunderstorm?" Sarah asked.

"Maybe it will go by us," said Granny. She put the book down. "It's bedtime," she said. Granny showed the girls up to the bedroom. She turned off the light over their beds.

Granny left. Sarah said to Julie, "I'm scared of thunderstorms—even in the city."

"So am I," said Julie.

They were quiet for a minute or two. Then Sarah said, "What if swamp halibuts are real? And what was the other thing?"

"Bush mackerel," said Julie. "But they're not."

"But if they were real," said Sarah, "what do you think they'd look like?"

"Like fish, I think," said Julie. "But maybe covered with fur and with feet like ducks."

"That's what I think," said Sarah.

The girls went to sleep. After a while Sarah sat up in her bed.

"Help! Help!" she cried.

"What's the matter?" asked Julie.

"I see swamp halibut and bush mackerel."

"You're dreaming," said Julie. "There's nothing here. I'll turn on the light."

But the light didn't work.

Just then the girls saw lightning and heard thunder.

PART TWO
The Thunderstorm

Julie was scared. She went into the hall. "Granny," she yelled, "Granny, where are you?"

Granny came with a flashlight.

"Our light doesn't work," said Julie.

"All of the lights in the house are out," said Granny. "Sometimes the lights go out in a storm. I thought I heard Sarah. Is something wrong?"

"She was dreaming about the bush mackerel and the swamp halibut."

"I really should think before I talk," said Granny. "Not everyone knows how to take what I say. It was only a joke."

Together they went into Sarah and Julie's room.

"See, Sarah," said Granny, turning the flashlight around the room. "There are no swamp halibut or bush mackerel here. And there never were."

"I was sure I saw them," Sarah said.

"You were dreaming," said Julie.

"I guess so," said Sarah. "But it's very strange. I can't even remember going to sleep."

"You know what I think," said Granny. "I think we should all forget about sleeping while this storm is going on."

She led them down to the living room. The flashlight gave them some light. They sat together at a table.

"When I was a girl," said Granny, "I was scared of thunderstorms, too. One summer I was at my grandmother's. There was a bad thunderstorm just like this one."

"I cried and put my head under the bedcovers.
But my grandmother made me get up. She made me
sit on her lap by a window. We looked out at
the storm. It was beautiful and exciting. I
remember hearing the first drops of rain the way
you can hear them now. And after that, I was
never scared again."

"Not even a little?" said Julie.

"Maybe just a little," said Granny.

"Can we look out the window at the storm?"
asked Sarah.

"If you'd like to," said Granny.

And so they did.

"It works," said Julie after a while. "I don't feel scared anymore."

"It's fun," said Sarah.

At last there was no more lightning. And the thunder sounded far away. The sound of rain made the girls feel like sleeping.

"Let's go to bed," said Julie.

"Yes, let's," said Sarah.

Granny went up to the bedroom again. The girls got into bed. Sarah asked Granny, "If swamp halibut and bush mackerel aren't real, who told you about them?"

"My grandmother," said Granny. "She's the same one who showed me how not to be afraid of thunderstorms."

"Did you believe in them when she told you?" asked Sarah.

"Just a little," said Granny.

"That's all I believed in them," said Sarah. "Just a little."

By morning the sun was shining. The bedside light was shining brightly, too. Julie got up. Sarah was still asleep.

Julie ran downstairs and ate breakfast
with Granny.

"Granny," said Julie, "I know you're not so
scared of thunderstorms and things. But aren't
you lonely sometimes here in the woods alone?"

"Lonely?" said Granny. "Sometimes I am, but
it's the way I want to live. Besides, the trees
and the ponds are like friends. And I have Trev."

"When I'm big, do you think I'll be like you?"
Julie asked Granny.

"What do you mean?" asked Granny.

"Oh, you know, brave and good at country
things?"

"You already are," said Granny.

Sarah got up and ate. Then she and Julie
played by the pond again. Sarah found a turtle
that she wanted to take home along with her small
frogs. Julie found a snake.

Julie's mother came to drive them home.

"Come again, Sarah," said Granny.

"I'd like to," Sarah said.

The girls sat in the back of the car on the way home. Very quietly Julie asked Sarah, "When you saw the swamp halibut and bush mackerel—in your dream, I mean—did they really have feet?"

"Oh, yes," said Sarah. She thought for a minute. "Only the bush mackerel was covered with fur. But the two of them had feet like ducks."

In the Country

I think people wonder
in the country much more
than they wonder in the city
with houses next door:

They see more world
in the country, more sky,
so there's much more space
for wondering. That's why!

— Aileen Fisher

Same Sound – Different Letters

Sometimes different letters stand for the same sound. All the words in each box below have the same vowel sound. But each of them is spelled with different letters.

s<u>ea</u> fr<u>ee</u> bel<u>ie</u>ve h<u>e</u> an<u>y</u>	m<u>y</u>stery p<u>i</u>n b<u>ui</u>ld b<u>u</u>sy b<u>ee</u>n
l<u>a</u>k<u>e</u> d<u>ay</u> r<u>ai</u>n th<u>ey</u> <u>eigh</u>t	k<u>e</u>pt fri<u>e</u>nd s<u>a</u>id h<u>ea</u>d <u>a</u>ny
g<u>o</u>ld kn<u>ow</u> b<u>oa</u>t st<u>o</u>n<u>e</u>	sk<u>y</u> d<u>i</u>nosaur r<u>i</u>de r<u>igh</u>t

Phoneme-Grapheme Relationships. Have the children read the words in each box. Point out the vowel sound common to all the words in the box and the different ways to spell it.

219

Dina Anastasio

Two Wishes

"I will win that contest," thought Ana when she saw the sign. "There is no question about it! I will win!"

PAPER AIRPLANE CONTEST
○ SATURDAY, 9 AM ○
SOUTH STREET SCHOOL
MAKE AN AIRPLANE THAT WILL FLY FARTHER THAN ANYONE'S.
WIN A RIDE IN A HOT-AIR BALLOON.

Ana had wanted a hot-air balloon ride for a long time. At first she had wanted the balloon to take her across the water, back to her friends. But it looked like that would never happen. So she had made another wish. She had wished she could find a friend here, in her new home.

By her next birthday, Ana's wish had come true. Ana had found a good friend. Louisa was her name. Now all Ana wished for was a ride in a balloon. And, if she won, that wish would come true, too.

That afternoon Ana went to the library. She took out a book on paper airplanes. When she got home, she found some paper. Ana went right to work. By that night she had made an airplane. It could fly from one side of the living room to the other. It was long and fast. But that wasn't enough.

"This airplane needs something," thought Ana. "I can't have an airplane that's just fast. My plane has to have class. It needs a few little things to help it out a bit."

The next day, the contest was the talk of Ana's school. Everyone, it seemed, had always dreamed of a ride in a balloon. And it was clear, too, that everyone planned to win.

Ana said nothing about her airplane. She didn't say a word about how fast it flew. She didn't tell of her plans to make it the most beautiful airplane in the contest. She tried not to talk about the contest at all. Louisa asked if she was going to be in it. Ana just said, "I guess so" and turned away. Louisa looked hurt, but Ana couldn't help that. She didn't want to talk about her idea with anyone—not even Louisa.

That night Ana got right to work. First she
put blue and green paper on the top of the
airplane. Then she wrote her name on the side.
Next she painted red and white bars on it.
Ana sat back to look at her work. "It's beautiful,"
she thought. "But it needs more." So she added
a long, red tail.

At last it was ready. How Ana wanted to call
Louisa and tell her about it! "It's not much
fun to have a great idea when you can't even
tell your best friend," she thought.

The next day was the day of the contest.
Ana went outside to fly her beautiful airplane.
She pulled back her arm and let the airplane go.
But it didn't fly. It didn't fly at all. It
just fell like a rock, to her feet. Ana picked
it up and tried again. Again it fell.

"It must be the wind," Ana thought. But
whichever way she turned, the plane would not fly.

Just then, Louisa came by with her plane.
It had no paint or paper or tail on it. Ana told
Louisa about her airplane not flying.

"Mind if I work on it?" Louisa asked.

"Go ahead," said Ana. "It's not going to
do me any good."

Louisa took off the tail and the blue and green paper. And then she flew it.

"Look at that!" cried Ana as it flew by her head. "Boy, was I silly! You can't fly an airplane with all that junk on it. That's why it wouldn't fly. I'll bet my plane can go farther than yours now."

Louisa didn't think so. Ana and Louisa threw their airplanes into the air. The two planes flew together for a few feet. But then Ana's came to a stop and fell. Louisa's flew another ten feet.

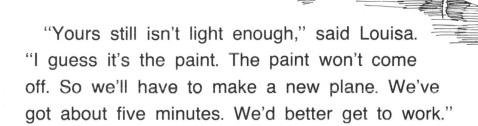

"Yours still isn't light enough," said Louisa. "I guess it's the paint. The paint won't come off. So we'll have to make a new plane. We've got about five minutes. We'd better get to work."

Ana and Louisa ran inside. Working side by side, they made another airplane. When they were through, they looked at the clock. There was no time to try it. And there was no time to think as they ran to the school.

Ana and Louisa were the last people to try out their planes. Louisa went first. She threw her airplane. It floated through the air. When it landed, it had gone farther than any of the other planes.

And then it was Ana's turn. She walked slowly over to the judges. She pulled back her arm. Before she knew it, the plane was gone. The wind caught it just right. The wind carried it farther and farther until, at last, it landed. She had won the contest!

At first Ana couldn't believe it. But then the judges led her over to the balloon. They helped her get on. As she waited for the balloon to move, she saw Louisa. Her friend was standing alone waving. Ana waved back. But as she did so, a sad feeling came over her.

"Ready?" a judge asked her.

But Ana was not ready. "No," she said.
"I can't go. I didn't make that plane alone.
My friend helped me. And she did most of the
work. So she should have the ride, not me."

Ana and Louisa took a ride together that day.
The wind felt good on their faces. The waves
broke quietly on the shore below. At one time,
Ana even thought that she could see her old home.

But the best thing about the ride was that
Ana and Louisa were together. Ana was very
happy. Her two wishes had come true. She had
had a balloon ride, and she had a friend.

Hurricanes and Birthday Cake

A REAL STORY BY ELIZABETH LEVY WITH PICTURES TAKEN BY HER FAMILY

My aunts, uncles, and cousins like to get together. When they do, they all talk. They talk about the time I ate the birthday cake. "And in the middle of a hurricane," they say. Then they laugh. I laugh, too. But I don't remember it. I wish I did. But I don't. You see, I was just two years old. It's hard to remember things that happened when you were two. It's hard, even when it was an exciting time.

My family tells me it happened one summer. It was hot where we lived. But it was not hot near the ocean. My aunt and uncle lived near the ocean. So they asked us to visit them. Mother took my brother and me there for a visit. Dad did not go with us. He was not home then. He was fighting in the Second World War.

My uncle worked in a hospital. He was
a doctor. He took care of men who were hurt
in the war. The men came to the hospital
from Europe. They were hurt on battlefields
in Europe. A lot of men were hurt in the Second
World War.

So we spent that summer near the ocean.
It was not hot there. And there were friends
to talk to. With Dad gone Mother was lonely.
She was happy to be with my aunt. My brother
was happy, too. He liked to visit with my
two cousins.

During the summer we spent most of our time on the beach. Mother took pictures of all of us. They show us as we swam in the ocean. They show us as we played on the beach. Now I think the ocean is scary. I must have thought so then, too. Mother says my brother was also afraid of it at first.

The doctors at the hospital needed more help. Mother and my aunt went there to help. They were gone a lot. When they were gone, Grandma took care of us. She took care of my brother, my two cousins, and me. We were a lot of trouble for her. Still Grandma seemed to like doing it.

Soon the summer was over. So was our visit. My brother had to go to school. So we had to go home. We planned to go, but we stayed a few more days. We stayed for Mother's birthday. My aunt and uncle did not want her to be home on that day. They did not want her to be lonely.

The day before Mother's birthday news came about the hurricane. A hurricane is a storm. It is a horrible storm. There are great winds. The winds move faster than the fastest cars. The winds shake down houses. They tear trees from the land. They push the ocean into big waves. Winds and water crash along together.

When they heard about the storm, people filled bags with sand. They put the bags around each house. The sandbags would help each house stand up in the storm. By night everyone felt safe. So my aunt made a cake. She made a birthday cake for Mother.

During the morning of the next day, there was great weather. Then it turned to hurricane weather. It was exciting at first. Then rain beat down hard. Winds crashed here and there. And the house started to shake. Now there was trouble. Could the house stand in this weather? Was it safe here?

It was some storm. If you were in the house during the storm, you could be killed by flood waters. If you went out, you could be killed by the wind. I was too small to know all this trouble. All I knew was that I saw a cake on the table. Somehow I climbed on the table. No one saw me do it. And there in the middle of the hurricane, I ate cake.

I was eating Mother's birthday cake when the police came. They came to help us out of the house. They started to take us to a safe place. Then they saw me. There I was with cake all over me. There was cake on my face. Cake was on my clothes. I even had cake in my hair. While my family worried about our trouble, I had a party.

"What's this!" laughed a policeman. "Is it a hurricane party?"

The policemen laughed. Mother laughed. They all laughed. Mother said that I made her feel brave. Now I don't know how I did that.

Two policemen carried Grandma. One man carried me. Somehow we all got out. We got out before the flood waters got to us. We were lucky.

The flood waters did get into the house. The house was ruined. But the policemen came in time to save us. If they had come later, we might not have made it out safely.

My family tells me that's what happened. I can't be sure. I was just two years old. I don't remember the hurricane.

Flying High

Have you ever been up in an airplane? If you have, then perhaps you've met some of these people.

Both of these people are pilots. The woman is a helicopter pilot. The man works for an airline. He flies planes all over the world.

Airplane pilots and their passengers depend on many other people.

They depend on mechanics to keep the airplane in perfect condition for flying.

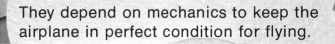

For safety, they depend on air traffic controllers and ramp agents.

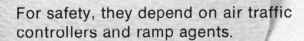

They depend on flight attendants to serve them while on board.

Wouldn't it be exciting to have one of these jobs?

Ramu and the Kite

MEHLLI GOBHAI

The Blue Kite

Ramu was eight. And eight was old enough to fly a kite. His father gave him two rupees for his first kite. With the rupees in his hand, Ramu ran to the kite store.

Ramu bought a kite with one rupee. It was blue with a bit of red on its tail. He bought string and a string holder with the other rupee. The string was coated with small bits of glass. Because of the glass, the string could be used to cut down another kite. The glass would turn Ramu's kite into a fighter.

That night Ramu's father showed him how to string a kite. First he found a small stick. With the stick he made holes in the paper. If the stick were too big, the holes would be too big. If the holes were too big, wind would tear the kite.

Next Ramu's father pushed the string through the holes. Then he knotted the string to hold it in place. The last thing he did was wind it on the holder.

When the kite was all set to fly, Ramu put it away. It was still eight days before Kite Day. And no boy would think of flying his kite before that day.

On the morning of Kite Day, Ramu watched the older boys go to the park with their kites. He knew he was not ready to go with them. So he went to the field behind his house with his father. He had to learn to fly a kite.

Ramu's father held the string. Ramu walked away from him with the kite. When the string was tight, Ramu's father said, "Now!" Ramu jumped into the air. He pushed the kite as far up as he could push it. For a minute, kite and boy were in the air. Then the boy landed on the grass. And the kite headed into the sky.

Now Ramu's father put the string into Ramu's hand. The boy was alone with his kite. The rest of the world seemed far away.

Soon Ramu's kite was so far up in the sky that he could hardly see it. The string felt tight. Then all at once the kite fell toward the earth. Ramu heard his father call, "Pull!"

Ramu pulled on the string. The kite righted itself. Then it headed into the open sky.

To Ramu it seemed only a few minutes before his father called, "Time to go home." Ramu started to pull his kite in. The kite seemed to fight him every bit of the way. At last Ramu held the kite in his arms again. But it would not be still. It was like a bird that wanted to be free.

Ramu took the kite to the field behind his house every day. After eight days, he knew he was ready to fly his kite with the other boys.

The Silver Kite

Ramu went to the park in the morning.
The sky above it was full of kites. Ramu
started to fly his blue kite. It did just
what Ramu wanted it to do. Soon it floated
along with the other kites.

All at once a big red kite headed toward
the blue kite. Ramu pulled at the string.
His blue kite climbed quickly into the sky.
The red kite missed cutting down Ramu's kite.
From now on Ramu would have to watch out.
He was in a battle with fighter kites.

Ramu saw the red kite float away from the others. He pulled the string of his kite. It went charging into battle. The sharp strings soon were wound around each other. Each boy tried to cut the string of the other boy's kite. All at once Ramu saw the red kite float away. It floated free in the sky. Ramu had won his first battle.

Some boys began to run after the red kite. They had long branches in their hands. Ramu saw one boy catch the red kite with one of the branches. He pulled the kite down from the sky. When he got it, he ran off with it.

Ramu looked up to see if his kite was safe. Out of nowhere, it seemed, came a white kite.

Before Ramu could make a move, the string of his kite was wound around the sharp string of the white kite. But this time Ramu was not ready. He pulled on the string, but there was no hope. Ramu saw his kite float off. The string was cut.

The wind pushed the kite into the branches of a tall tree. Even then the blue kite tried to get away. But at last the kite moved no more. It lay still. Ramu saw that the blue paper was ruined. He knew that in a few days there would be nothing left of his beautiful kite.

Ramu walked slowly home. When his mother saw him, she guessed what had happened and left him alone.

That night Ramu told his father the story. "I will give you another rupee to get a new kite," his father said.

"I will never fly another kite," said Ramu.

Ramu lay awake in his bed that night. He lay awake and watched the moon. It floated in the sky like a great silver kite. At last he fell asleep. And he had a dream.

There was a bright light at the window, and before Ramu was a kite. It was silver like the moon. And it was two times as big as Ramu. It seemed to be calling to him without words.

Ramu opened the window, and the next thing he knew, he was holding on to the silver kite. They were flying through the air with a sound like the wind in a forest. Up and up the kite took Ramu until he could look down on all the roofs of the town. Soon he was above the clouds, and he could hardly see the lights below him.

The kite seemed to be telling Ramu
many things—things he could not really
understand. "I am all kites," it seemed
to say. "I am your blue kite and the red
kite and the white kite. I am all the kites
you will ever fly. I am even the
kite you will dream of but never own."

Ramu and the kite were flying right
at the moon. It came closer and closer
until Ramu couldn't look any longer.
With a sharp cry, he was awake.

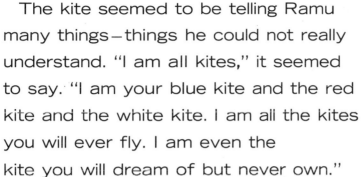

It was morning already. The sky was
blue. Near Ramu lay a silver rupee,
as round and bright as the full moon.

Amy's Goose

Efner Tudor Holmes

Amy was standing in the garden when she heard
the cry she had been waiting for all fall.

Her face turned toward the sky. There she saw
the long **V** of the wild geese. Their call grew
louder and louder as they flew closer. Amy
knew that they would spend the night on the
shores of the lake.

By morning, they would be off again on their
long journey to the warm South. When they left,
Amy would feel lonely. For Amy was an only
child, and the wild geese were her friends.

X By now the geese were over her head in the sky. Soon they would land in the lake and on its shores.

She turned to see her father walking toward her.

"Well, little one," he said. "I see your friends have come back. As soon as we have dinner, we'll get that sack of corn for them."

X "Aren't they beautiful?" Amy asked him. "And there are a lot more of them this year."

Her father smiled at her. "That's because they have heard about a lake where a little girl will be waiting with a lot of good corn," he teased her.

After dinner, Amy and her father walked toward the lake with the sack of corn.

All at once they heard the wild honking of one goose. The honking grew louder and louder. Then the other geese began to pick up its cry. Amy could hear them beat their wings on the water. As she ran down the field, she saw many geese fly up into the air in fright. Others stayed on the shores, standing with their long necks stretched to the sand.

"It's a fox," her father cried. "Look, he's got one!"

Amy's father dropped the sack of corn, picked up a rock, and threw it at the fox. Amy ran at the fox yelling. The fox let go of the goose and ran away.

✗ But the goose lay still. On her white neck,
Amy saw blood. The blood was spreading. Amy
got down on her knees and carefully picked up
the big bird. The goose beat her wings in
fright and tried to fly away. But she was too
weak to put up much of a fight. Soon the goose
lay quietly, her wings falling over Amy's legs
and onto the sand. Amy's father got down beside
them to look.

✗ "It may not really be as bad as it looks," he
said. "I think we can save her. Let's get her
up to the barn."

When Amy went to look at the goose the next
morning, she was surprised to see the wild bird
standing up and eating. The goose didn't seem
as weak as she had the day before.

X Amy walked slowly up to the goose and held out
her hand. But the bird beat her wings in fright
and went to a far corner. The goose and the
girl sat for a few minutes looking at each other.

"It's all right," Amy said. "You're safe here."

X Amy spent most of the rest of the day with the
goose. Late in the afternoon, the wild bird
ate some corn from her hand. Still later, when
Amy held the bird in her arms, the goose started
to gabble in a friendly way.

A very special feeling for the big wild bird had started to grow in Amy.

"The goose is quite friendly now," she thought. "Maybe I can keep her. It would be nice to have a wild bird for a pet."

The next few days, Amy spent most of her time taking care of the goose. One late afternoon, Amy and the goose were out in the garden. All at once, they heard the cry of another goose. Amy looked up to see a bird flying over the barn. She heard a wild honking cry.

Amy's goose stood looking up into the sky at the other bird. Then she began to answer his call and beat her wings.

Amy saw the rest of the geese on the lake. They had not started their journey to the South! They were waiting for her goose. "That must be her mate calling to her!" Amy thought.

"Come on," she said to the goose, "I'm going to put you in the barn. You're not well enough for flying yet. You're still weak. Next spring your friends will be back."

Amy put the goose back into the barn. Then she closed the door and went to help her mother fix dinner.

After dinner Amy felt upset. The warm house seemed to hold her in, like a cage. She thought of the wild bird she had put in the barn. She knew that the goose *was* really well enough for the long journey now. She thought of the other goose flying alone over the barn, calling to his mate.

Amy went out of the house. She walked through the garden and down to the lake. For a long time, she watched the geese. A few would fly up and call to the others. Then they would drop back into the water. Other geese stood together on the shores as if holding a meeting.

All at once the geese flew up into the sky together. Their cry filled the air. Amy watched them fall into the long **V** of the wild geese. She would see no more geese until spring. Winter was coming. Amy knew it, and the geese knew it, too.

The long **V** began to grow smaller. Then Amy saw one bird drop out and begin flying back. Amy knew where he was headed.

Amy began running up the field. As she came to the barn, she heard the cry of the goose in the cold air. She heard the honking from the barn.

Amy opened the barn door. The wild goose
was right behind it. She had been trying to
get out. When the goose saw Amy, she stretched
out her long neck and started to gabble.

Amy got down on her knees. She put her arms
around the big bird. She began to cry. She
held the bird close to her. She wished the goose
would stay. Then she picked up the wild bird and
slowly carried her into the night.

They stood together for a few minutes. Then
the goose set up a cry. She began to run and
beat her wings.

Amy watched the goose fly into the sky. Her mate joined her, and together they flew away.

The girl stood alone in the night. She had stopped crying. She felt the cold earth under her feet.

Amy thought happily of spring. Then she would be standing by the lake watching the wild geese fly over and into the water.

sing little bird

Sing, little bird,
when the skies are blue;
Sing, for the world
has need of you;
Sing, when the skies
are overcast;
Sing when the rain
is falling fast.

Sing, happy heart,
when the sun is warm;
Sing in the winter's
coldest storm;
Sing little songs,
O heart so true;
Sing, for the world
has need of you.

—Maria Hastings

CHARLIE THE TRAMP

RUSSELL HOBAN

"Well, well," said Grandfather Beaver one day when he came to visit. "Charlie is getting to be a big boy."

"Yes, he is," said Father. "He is coming right along."

Grandfather smiled at Charlie and took a quarter out of his vest pocket.

"What are you going to be when you grow up, Charlie?" asked Grandfather.

"I am going to be a tramp," said Charlie.

"A *tramp!*" said Mother.

"A *tramp!*" said Father.

"A *tramp!*" said Grandfather, and he put the quarter back in his vest pocket.

"Yes," said Charlie, "I am going to be a tramp."

"I am surprised to hear that," said Father. "Your grandfather has been doing beaver work for many years, and I, too, am a beaver, but you want to be a tramp."

"That is how it is nowadays," said Grandfather, shaking his head. "When I was young, children did not want to be tramps."

"I don't think Charlie really wants to be a tramp," said Mother.

"Yes, I do," said Charlie. "Tramps don't have to learn how to chop down trees and how to roll logs and how to build dams."

"Tramps don't have to practice swimming and diving and holding their breath under water.

"Nobody looks to see if their teeth are sharp. Nobody looks to see if their fur is oiled.

"Tramps carry sticks with little bundles tied to them. They sleep in a field when the weather is nice, and when it rains, they sleep in a barn.

"Tramps just tramp around and have a good time. And when they want something to eat, they do little jobs for anybody that wants little jobs done."

"I have lots of little jobs for you to do," said Father. "You can help me cut saplings for our winter food. You can help me dig extra tunnels for our lodge. And, of course, the dam always needs repairs."

"That is not little jobs," said Charlie. "That's hard work."

"When I was young," said Grandfather, "children did hard work. Nowadays all they want to do is little jobs."

"Well," said Father, "if Charlie wants to be a tramp, then I think he should be a tramp. I think we should not stand in his way."

"The weather is nice and warm now," said Charlie. "May I start sleeping in fields?"

"All right," said Mother.

Charlie tied up some cookies and some candy in a handkerchief. Then he tied the handkerchief to a stick, and he was ready to go.

"Now it is time for me to be on the road and away," said Charlie.

"Good-by, Mr. Tramp," said Father and Grandfather.

"Good-by, Mr. Tramp," said Mother. "Come home in time for breakfast, and don't forget to brush your teeth tonight."

"Good-by," said Charlie. "Tramps don't brush their teeth."

He got into his little boat, rowed across the pond, and tramped off down the road, while Mother and Father and Grandfather waved to him.

"Now that I think of it," said Grandfather, "I wanted to be a tramp when I was little, just like Charlie."

"So did I," said Father.

"That is how beavers are," said Mother. "Some of them want to be tramps."

Charlie tramped down the road, kicking a stone and whistling a tramping song as he went.

He looked at the blue hills far away, and he listened to cowbells tinkling in distant meadows.

Sometimes he stopped to throw stones at telephone poles, and sometimes he sat under a tree and watched the clouds roll by.

Charlie kept tramping until it was almost sundown, and then he picked a field to sleep in. He picked a field where daisies grew and the grass and the clover smelled sweet.

Charlie untied his little bundle and took out some cookies and some candy, and he ate them while the stars came out.

"Being a tramp is nice," said Charlie to himself, and he went to sleep.

Mother was watching for him at the window the next morning when he rowed across the pond.

"Here comes Charlie," she said to Father, "with his fur every which way and a bundle of daisies on his stick."

"Good morning," said Charlie when Mother opened the door. And he gave her the daisies. "Do you have a little job I can do for my breakfast?" he said.

"You can bail out the big rowboat," said Father. "That will be a nice little job for you."

"All right," said Charlie. "And then I will eat my breakfast on the back steps, because that is how we tramps do it."

So Charlie bailed out the rowboat. And while he was eating his breakfast on the back steps. Father came and sat down beside him. "How do you like being a tramp?" he said.

"I like it fine," said Charlie. "It is a lot easier than being a beaver."

"How did you sleep last night?" said Father.

"Fine," said Charlie. "But something kept waking me up."

"Was it anything scary?" said Father.

"No," said Charlie, "it was something nice, but I don't know what it was. I will have to listen for it again tonight."

Then Charlie rowed across the pond and went off down the road, whistling his tramping song.

Charlie tramped all day. He listened to the birds singing. He smelled the flowers that grew by the side of the road. Sometimes he stopped to pick blackberries. Sometimes he walked along the top rails of fences.

At lunchtime and dinnertime Charlie went home and did little jobs for his lunch and his dinner.

He stacked winter saplings in the basement for his lunch. And for his dinner he helped his father fix a broken plank in the boat landing.

After dinner Charlie went back to the field where the clover and the daisies grew. Charlie ate his cookies and his candy, and he listened for the sound he had heard the night before.

Charlie heard the frogs and the crickets singing in the quiet of the night, and he heard something else. He heard a trickling, tickling kind of a little song that had no words.

The trickling, tickling song made Charlie want to hear it better. So he got up and went down to the trees where the sound was coming from.

He saw a little stream that sang as it ran in the moonlight, and he sat down and listened to the song again. But the sound of the trickling kept tickling Charlie, and he could not sit still.

So he took off his clothes, and he dived into the stream and swam around inside the song the water was singing.

Then Charlie climbed out and cut down a little tree that was growing on the bank. When the tree fell down, he rolled it into the water.

Charlie took a deep breath and swam to the bottom of the stream with the tree and stuck it in the mud so that it would not float away.

Then he listened to the song of the water, and he liked it better than he had before. So Charlie cut down some more trees, and he began to make a little dam to keep all the water from trickling away.

Charlie worked on his dam all night. And by morning the stream had widened into a pond. Then the song of the water stopped tickling Charlie, and he said, "Now I guess I can go back to sleep."

So he brushed his teeth to keep them sharp. He oiled his fur to keep it waterproof. And he went to sleep in an old hollow tree by his new pond.

Charlie slept right through breakfast time, and Mother began to worry when she did not see him.

"I am sure Charlie is all right," said Father, "but I think we should look for him anyhow." And he went down to the boat landing and slapped the water with his tail, WHACK!

WHACK! answered Grandfather with his tail, and he came over to see what was the matter.

"I never did think any good would come of letting that boy run off to be a tramp," said Mother.

"That's how it is nowadays," said Grandfather. "Boys run off, and no good comes of it."

So Mother and Father and Grandfather went looking for Charlie, and after a while they came to the new pond. But they did not see Charlie sleeping in the hollow tree.

"I don't remember seeing a pond around here before," said Grandfather.

"Neither do I," said Father. "It must be a new one."

"That's a pretty good pond," said Grandfather. "I wonder who made it?"

"I don't know," said Father. "You think maybe Harry Beaver might have done it?"

"No," said Grandfather. "Harry always makes a sloppy dam, and this one's not sloppy at all."

"What about old Zeb Beaver?" said Father. "Zeb always makes a good-looking dam."

"No," said Grandfather. "Zeb never makes a round pond like this one. Zeb always likes a long-shaped pond."

"You're right," said Father. "He does."

"You know," said Mother to Father, "this pond looks like the ponds you make."

"She's right," said Grandfather. "It does."

"That's funny," said Father. "I didn't make it. I wonder who did?"

"I did," said Charlie, waking up and coming out of the hollow tree. "That's my pond."

"That's your pond?" said Father.

"That's my pond," said Charlie.

"I thought you were a tramp," said Grandfather. "Tramps don't make ponds."

"Well," said Charlie, "sometimes I like to tramp around, and sometimes I like to make ponds."

"Any tramp that can make a pond like that is going to be some beaver one of these days," said Father.

"That's how it is nowadays," said Grandfather. "You never know when a tramp will turn out to be a beaver." And he took the quarter out of his vest pocket and gave it to Charlie.

"Thank you," said Charlie. "Where's Mother?"

But Mother had run back to the boat, rowed across the pond as fast as she could, and had flapjacks and maple syrup ready on the table when the men got home.

The Beaver

    The beaver is fat,
and his tail is so flat
that it closely resembles an oar.
He's known for his teeth,
those on top and beneath,
and he lives just a trifle offshore.

    He nibbles on trees
as a mouse nibbles cheese
with incisors as sharp as a knife.
And with dexterous tricks
builds a house out of sticks
along with his children and wife.

—Jack Prelutsky

287

Glossary

This glossary gives the pronunciations and meanings of some of the words used in this book.

The pronunciation is shown just after the word in this way: a•ble (ā′ bəl). The letters and signs are pronounced as shown in the words listed below.

If the word has more than one syllable, as in the example, a heavy accent mark ′ is placed after the syllable that receives the heaviest stress.

PRONUNCIATION KEY

a	hat	i	it	ou	out	w	will
ā	face	ī	ice	p	paper	y	yes
ä	father	j	jam	r	run	z	zoo
b	bad	k	kind	s	say	zh	treasure
ch	child	l	land	sh	she		
d	did	m	me	t	tell	ə stands for
e	let	n	no	th	thin	a in about
ē	be	ng	long	ŦH	then	e in given
ėr	her	o	hot	u	cut	i in family
f	fat	ō	open	ů	pull	o in button
g	go	ô	or	ü	June	u in walrus
h	he	oi	oil	v	very	

The pronunciation key, syllable breaks, and phonetic respellings in this glossary are adapted from the eighth edition of the *Thorndike-Barnhart Beginning Dictionary*. Users of previous editions or other dictionaries will find other symbols for some words.

A

A•bu (ä′ bü)

aye (ī) yes; used often to answer a command: *Aye, aye, Captain!*

B

bail (bāl) throw water out of a boat with a bucket, pail, or any other container

bank (bangk) 1. ground on the side of a river or lake. 2. place of business for handling money

barn (bärn) building for storing hay and grain and for sheltering cows and horses

base•ment (bās′ mənt) the lowest floor of a building, partly or wholly below ground

bat•tle•field (bat′ l fēld′) a place where a battle is fought or has been fought

bea•ver (bē′ vər) an animal with soft fur, a broad flat tail, and feet adapted to swimming: *Beavers live both in water and on land and build dams across streams.*

bed•cov•ers (bed′ kuv′ ərz) covers for beds

be•side (bi sīd′) 1. by the side of, close to, near: *Grass grows beside the fence.* 2. compared with: *The wolf seems tame beside the tiger.*

bis•cuit (bis′ kit) a flat, dry cake

black•ber•ry (blak′ ber′ ē) the small, black fruit of certain bushes or vines

breath (breth) the air drawn into and forced out of the lungs

build (bild) make by putting materials together: *Birds build nests.*

bun•dle (bun′ dl) a number of things tied or wrapped together

C

cam•el (kam′ əl) a large, four-footed mammal with a long neck, cushioned feet, and a hump on its back

cam•paign (kam pān′) things that are done in order to get something or to reach a goal: *Our club had a campaign to find books for the hospital.*

---

hat, fāce, fäther, let, bē, hèr, it, īce, hot, ōpen, ôr, oil, out, cut, pùll, Jüne, thin, ŦHen;
ə stands for *a* in about, *e* in given, *i* in family, *o* in button, *u* in walrus.

cap•tain (kap′ tən) 1. leader of a group; chief. 2. commander of a ship: *The captain ordered the sailors to clean the deck.* 3. officer in the armed services

cen•tral (sen′ trəl) of the center; forming the center

chest (chest) 1. large box with a lid, used for holding things. 2. part of a person's or an animal's body enclosed by ribs

cit•y (sit′ ē) a large, important town

clo•ver (klō′ vər) a plant with leaves of three small leaves and sweet-smelling, rounded heads of red, white, or purple flowers

col•lec•tion (kə lek′ shən) a bringing together; coming together

con•test (kon′ test) trial of skill to see who or which can win

Con•us ber•nar•di (kōn′ us bėr när′ d ī)

cous•in (kuz′ n) son or daughter of one's uncle or aunt

crick•et (krik′ it) a black insect in the grasshopper family

Cu•ba (kyü′ bə) island in the West Indies

D

dai•sy (dā′ zē) a wild flower with white, pink, or yellow petals around a yellow center

dam (dam) a wall built to hold back the water of a stream or river

des•ert (dez′ ərt) place without water and trees: *A desert is usually sandy.*

Des•ta (des′ tä)

dif•fer•ent (dif′ ər ənt) 1. unusual: *Our teacher is quite different; she never gives us any homework.* 2. not alike: *People have different names.*

dis•tant (dis′ tənt) far away: *The sun is distant from the earth.*

dol•phin (dol′ fən) a sea animal much like a small whale: *A dolphin has a snout like a beak and is very smart.*

down•town (doun′ toun′) to or in the main part or business part of a town or city

dream (drēm) something thought, felt, or seen during sleep

E

earth (ėrth) 1. planet on which we live. 2. soil; ground

eel (ēl) a long, slippery fish shaped like a snake

e·lec·tion (i lek′ shən) choosing by vote

en·gine (en′ jən) 1. a machine that gives off power for working, often for moving other machines. 2. a machine that pulls other cars of a railroad train

Eur·ope (yŭr′ əp) continent east of the Atlantic Ocean and west of Asia

ex·tra (ek′ strə) beyond what is usual, expected, or needed

F

fan (fan) 1. something used to move the air in a room or around the face. 2. someone very interested in a sport, in the movies or television, or in a special person.

feath·er (feтH′ ər) the light, thin growth that covers a bird's skin: *Because feathers are soft and light, they are used to fill pillows.*

field (fēld) a piece of flat land with few trees

fin (fin) one of the movable winglike or fanlike parts of a fish's body

flag·pole (flag′ pōl′) pole from which a flag is flown

flap·jack (flap′ jak′) a flat cake made of thin batter and cooked on both sides

flash·light (flash′ līt′) an electric light that can be carried and that runs on batteries

float (flōt) stay on top of or be held up by air, water, or other liquid: *A cork will float, but a stone sinks.*

flood (flud) a great flow of water over what is usually dry land

fo·rest (fôr′ ist) thick woods; large woodland

Fu·mi·o (fü′ mē ō)

fur (fėr) the soft hair covering the skin of many animals

G

gar·den (gärd′ n) 1. piece of ground used for growing vegetables, flowers, or fruits. 2. take care of a garden

goat (gōt) a small animal with horns: *A goat is raised for its milk.*

---

hat, fāce, fäther, let, bē, hėr, it, īce, hot, ōpen, ôr, oil, out, cut, pùll, Jüne, thin, тHen; ə stands for *a* in about, *e* in given, *i* in family, *o* in button, *u* in walrus.

gro•cer•ies (grō′ sər ēz) food and household supplies sold by a grocer

H

hal•i•but (hal′ ə bət) a very large flatfish, much used for food; halibuts sometimes weigh several hundred pounds

hand•ker•chief (hang′ kər chif) a soft square of cloth used for wiping the nose, face, or hands

hand•y (han′ dē) 1. easy to reach or use: *There were handy shelves near the kitchen sink.* 2. skillful with the hands: *He is handy with tools.*

head (hed) move toward: *Our ship will head south.*

head•quar•ters (hed′ kwôr′ tərz) 1. place from which the chief of an army or police force sends out orders. 2. the main office

hol•low (hol′ ō) empty; with a hole inside

hos•pi•tal (hos′ pi təl) place for the care of the sick or injured

hunt•er (hun′ tər) 1. person who hunts. 2. horse or dog trained for hunting

hur•ri•cane (hėr′ ə kān) storm with violent wind and, usually, very heavy rain

I

ice•berg (īs′ berg′) a very big piece of ice floating in the ocean: *The iceberg was much bigger than our ship.*

i•de•a (ī dē′ ə) a belief, plan, or picture in the mind

is•land (ī′ lənd) body of land surrounded by water

J

Ji•ma (jē′ mä)

jour•ney (jėr′ nē) a trip: *We will take a journey south this winter.*

judge (juj) person chosen to settle a dispute or to decide who wins a race or contest

K

knife (nīf) a thin, flat metal blade fastened in a handle so that it can be used to cut or spread

knot (not) 1. tangle. 2. a fastening made by tying or twining together pieces of ropes, strings, or cords

L

lay (lā) put down; place or set

learn (lėrn) find out; come to know

li•brar•y (lī′ brer′ ē) a place where a collection of books, magazines, and newspapers is kept.

light•house (līt′ hous′)
tower with a bright
light that shines far
over the water

light•ning (līt′ ning) flash of elec-
tricity in the sky

lis•ten (lis′ n) try to hear

lodge (loj) place to live in; house,
especially a small house

M

mack•er•el (mak′ ər əl)
a salt-water fish of
the North Atlantic,
much used for food

ma•ple (mā′ pəl) tree
grown for shade, its
wood, or its sap

may•or (mā′ ər) person at the head
of a clty or town government

mead•ow (med′ ō) a piece of grassy
land: *A meadow is used to grow
hay.*

mes•sage (mes′ ij) words sent from
someone to someone else

mi•cro•phone
(mī′ krə fōn) instru-
ment for making
sounds louder or for
sending sounds out
over the air

min•ute (min′ it) 1. 60 seconds. 2. a
short time

miss (mis) 1. fail to hit. 2. fail to
catch. 3. notice the absence of

mon•key (mung′ kē) a
small animal with a
long tail

mu•se•um (myü zē′ əm) a place
where collections of things having
to do with art or other subjects
are kept and shown: *We saw paint-
ings at the museum.*

N

neigh•bor (nā′ bər), someone who
lives next door or nearby

no•tice (nō′ tis) see; give attention
to

O

o•a•sis (ō ā′ sis) a spot
in the desert where
there is water

o•cean (ō′ shən) the great body of
salt water that covers almost three
fourths of the earth's surface

Olm•sted (ōm′ sted),
Fred•er•ick (fred′ ə rik)

out•let (out′ let) place
in a wall for inserting
an electric plug

o•ver•night (ō′ vər nīt′) during the
night; for the night

---

hat, fāce, fäther, let, bē, her, it, īce, hot, open, ôr, oil, out, cut, pull, Jüne, thin, ŦHen;
ə stands for *a* in about, *e* in given, *i* in family, *o* in button, *u* in walrus.

P

pan•try (pan′ trē) small room where food and dishes are kept

patch•work (pach′ wėrk′) pieces of cloth of different colors that have been sewn together

pig•eon (pij′ ən) bird with a plump body and short legs

Pip•sa (pip′ sä)

plank (plangk) a long, flat piece of wood thicker than a board

plant (plant) put in the ground to grow

plug (plug) 1. device to make an electrical connection. 2. piece of wood or other things used to stop up a hole

pool (pül) 1. tank of water to swim or bathe in. 2. a small pond. 3. puddle

pre•tend (pri tend′) make believe

prom•ise (prom′ is) words said or written, binding a person to do or not to do something

Q

quar•ter (kwôr′ tər) 1. a copper and nickel coin of the United States and Canada worth 25 cents. 2. one of four equal parts

quilt (kwilt) cover for a bed, usually made of two pieces of cloth with a soft pad between, held in place by stitching

R

rail (rāl) bar of wood or of metal

ral•ly (ral′ ē) coming together; meeting of many people

Ra•mu (rä mü′)

ray (rā) line or beam of light

re•mem•ber (ri mem′ bər) call back to mind; keep in mind

re•pair (ri par′) act of putting in good condition again

row•boat (rō′ bōt′) boat moved by oars

ru•in (rü′ ən) spoil; destroy

ru•pee (rü′ pē) money used in India and Pakistan

S

sand•bag (sand′ bag′) bag filled with sand and used to build walls to protect a place

sand•wich (sand′ wich) two or more slices of bread with meat, jelly, cheese, or some other filling between them

sap•ling (sap′ ling) a young tree

sci•en•tist (sī′ ən tist) person who has expert knowledge of some branch of science

sea•wa•ter (sē′ wô′ tər) water in or from the sea

seem (sēm) look like; appear to be

shim•mer (shim′ ər) shine or flash

shore (shôr) land at the edge of a sea, lake, or large river

sight (sīt) 1. act of seeing. 2. thing seen

sil•ver (sil′ vər) a shining white precious metal: *Silver is used to make coins, spoons, knives, and forks.*

since (sins) 1. from the time that; from the time when. 2. because: *Since you feel tired, you should rest.*

slop•py (slop′ ē) careless

snow•plow
(snō′ plou′) machine used to move snow off a road, tracks, or driveway

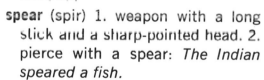

spear (spir) 1. weapon with a long stick and a sharp-pointed head. 2. pierce with a spear: *The Indian speared a fish.*

spring (spring) 1. a small stream of water coming from the earth. 2. a leap or jump

spy•glass (spī′ glas′) small instrument for making things that are far away seem closer and larger

stack (stak) pile high

still (stil) without motion; without noise

stream (strēm) flow of water in a channel or bed: *A small river may be called a stream.*

sun•down (sun′ doun′) sunset: *We'll be home by sundown.*

sun•flow•er
(sun′ flou′ ər) a tall plant having large yellow flowers with brown centers

swamp (swomp) wet, soft land: *The farmer will drain the swamp so that he can plant crops there.*

syr•up (sir′ əp) a sweet, thick liquid

T

takeoff (tāk′ ôf′) the leaving of the ground in leaping or in beginning a flight in an aircraft

Ta•ro (tä′ rō)

tease (tēz) to pick on, bother, or pester

teeth (tēth) more than one tooth

tent (tent) a movable shelter made of cloth or skins supported by a pole or poles

---

hat, fāce, fäther, let, bē, hėr, it, īce, hot, ōpen, ôr, oil, out, cut, pùll, Jūne, thin, ŦHen; ə stands for *a* in about, *e* in given, *i* in family, *o* in button, *u* in walrus.

thun•der (thun′ dər) a loud noise that often follows a flash of lightning

thun•der•storm (thun′ dər stôrm′) storm with thunder and lightning

tin•kle (ting′ kəl) make short, light, ringing sounds: *Little bells tinkle.*

tramp (tramp) someone who goes about begging: *A tramp came to the door and asked for food.*

trick•le (trik′ əl) fall in drops or in a small stream: *Tears trickle down her cheeks.*

trip (trip) 1. stumble and fall. 2. make a mistake. 3. take light, quick steps

tun•nel (tun′ l) underground passage: *The railroad passes under the mountain through a tunnel.*

U

un•der•stand (un′ dər stand′) get the meaning of

V

vest (vest) a piece of clothing without sleeves, usually worn under a suit coat

vil•lage (vil′ ij) group of houses, usually smaller than a town

vote (vōt) formally express a wish or choice: *He voted for the new school.*

W

wade (wād) walk through water, snow, sand, or mud: *Wade across a brook.*

war (wôr) fighting carried on by armed force between nations or parts of a nation

wa•ter•proof (wô′ tər prüf′) that will not let water through

wave (wāv) 1. move back and forth: *I'll wave the flag.* **2. a moving hill of water**

weath•er (weŦH′ ər) condition of the air around and above a certain person or place

whale (hwāl) animal shaped like a huge fish and living in the sea

which•ev•er (hwich ev′ ər) any one; any that: *Buy whichever hat you like.*

whis•tle (hwis′ əl) 1. make a clear, shrill sound. 2. instrument for making a whistling sound

wid•en (wīd′ n) make or become wide or wider

won•der (wun′ dər) be curious about; wish to know

wound (wound) twisted or turned around something